TRAVEL CAREER DEVELOPMENT

Student Workbook

8th Edition

Patricia J. Gagnon, CTC
Shelly M. Houser, CTC

TheTravelinstitute

Printed in Canada

Table of Contents

Preface

The *Travel Career Development Student Workbook* provides exercises that correspond to each chapter in the *Travel Career Development* textbook. The exercises are designed to reinforce the information you need to know in order to achieve the chapter objectives, to give you a good idea of your understanding of the chapter, and to enhance your understanding of the textbook by having you do further thinking and research.

What Is in the Workbook

The worksheets in Part 1 of the workbook offer many types of exercises. For example, there are exercises that call on you to

- define key terms.
- search the Web.
- apply or develop your knowledge of geography.
- recall airline and airport codes.
- read schedules.
- analyze tour brochures.
- compare travel products.
- develop critical analysis skills.
- solve problems.
- apply what you have learned to possible situations.
- evaluate your own interests and skills.

Part 2 of the workbook provides excerpts from important travel resources such as the *Official Hotel Guide,* Amtrak schedules, the *Thomas Cook European Timetable,* and tour and cruise brochures. Many worksheets include exercises that give you practice using these excerpts in order to ensure that you become proficient in working with the standard resources relied on by all segments of the travel industry.

How to Study *Travel Career Development*

A good approach to studying *Travel Career Development* is to concentrate on the text first. If your instructor assigns a chapter of the text and the corresponding chapter in the workbook, you may be tempted to first make sure you "get your homework done," going directly to the workbook and trying to answer the questions. We suggest you first concentrate on mastering the chapter:

- Look at the chapter outline and objectives first.
- Preview the chapter, skimming the pages and noticing the major headings. Ask yourself if you know anything about these topics already.
- Read over the key terms at the end of the chapter. Which ones do you know something about? Which ones are new?
- As you read through the chapter, highlight key points or those you might have questions about.
- Stop periodically to check that you have understood and can recall what you've read; doing so helps learning. Instead of reading straight through a chapter, stop after every major head and quiz yourself. The Check-Ups in the textbook help you do that. Although they're not intended to summarize an entire section, they review some key points. Try completing each item yourself after you read the introductory statement. If you can't, go back over the section. You might also use the Check-Ups to help you review for tests.
- Try reading just the first part of the On the Spot boxes; hide the second part of the box with a card or your hand. See how you would deal with the scenario

described before going on to read the second part of the box. (Don't be discouraged, though. Some of the boxes present issues not addressed in the text of the chapter.)

■ If you see a term in **boldface italic,** it's an important word, one that you should remember and be able to define. You can find definitions not only in the chapter where the term is printed in bold italic but also in the textbook's Glossary. Other important terms are printed in italics.

■ Don't forget the Chapter Highlights in the Chapter Wrap-Up. They should help you consolidate your mastery of the chapter and check your understanding, as well as review for tests.

Now you are ready to tackle the exercises in the *Travel Career Development Student Workbook.* The first worksheet in each chapter asks that you define the new terms in that chapter of the textbook. You don't need to give technical definitions. Put the definitions into your own words or the words you might use with clients. Going over these terms is one of the best ways to do a crash review before a test.

Some exercises in the workbook ask that you use outside sources such as newspaper ads, phone conversations with suppliers, or interviews. Look ahead to see which of these exercises you can plan time for. Not all exercises will be done by all classes—some require major course projects. Your instructor will guide you.

One worksheet in each chapter involves the Internet. The goals of these worksheets are to make sure that you

are comfortable using the Internet and that you become familiar with the information on major travel Web sites. These goals are much more important than finding the correct answer to a particular question, because answers may change month to month and sometimes day to day. Furthermore, some sites may change their addresses, and others may cease to function or to be current.

Be flexible in finding information. If the problems working with one Web site seem to be insurmountable, see if you can find another site with the same information. Don't be bogged down on one question, however; it may be better to go on to another and find out the next day if your fellow classmates experienced the same problem.

As you complete these worksheets on the use of technology, make your own lists of favorite Web sites that you might want to use in the future. Also, as you work on the other worksheets, you might want to write the answers on a separate sheet of paper. In that way you can use the workbook (without having the answers staring you in the face) to test yourself before taking classroom quizzes, finals, the Travel Career Development Test, or the National TAP Test.

The last worksheet in each chapter is entitled "Critical Thinking." It is designed to allow you to exercise your ability to examine various topics relevant to the travel industry by gathering information on the subject and offering your own opinions or predictions.

Good luck in using this workbook to learn the course objectives and to reach your personal goals in the travel industry.

Part 1:
Worksheets

Name _____   Date _____

Directions: Define the following terms.

1. ASTA _____

   _____

2. Benefit _____

   _____

3. Business travel _____

   _____

4. Close _____

   _____

5. Commission _____

   _____

6. Commodity _____

   _____

7. Conference system _____

   _____

8. Corporate travel _____

   _____

9. Demographic segmentation _____

   _____

10. Dependables _____

   _____

11. Distributor _____

   _____

12. Feature _____

   _____

(continued)

13. High season _____

_____

14. Hospitality industry _____

_____

15. Incentive travel _____

_____

16. Leisure travel _____

_____

17. Low season _____

_____

18. Marketing _____

_____

19. Market segmentation _____

_____

20. Meeting travel _____

_____

21. NTO _____

_____

22. Online travel agency _____

_____

23. Override _____

_____

24. Personal selling _____

_____

25. Preferred supplier relationship _____

_____

Name   Date

26. Price segmentation _____

_____

27. Professional _____

_____

28. Psychographic segmentation _____

_____

29. Qualifying _____

_____

30. Selling _____

_____

31. Shoulder season _____

_____

32. Special-interest travel _____

_____

33. Supplier _____

_____

34. Supporting businesses and organizations _____

_____

35. Target market _____

_____

36. TIA _____

_____

37. Travel agency _____

_____

38. Travel counselor _____

_____

(continued)

39. Usage segmentation _____

_____

40. Venturers _____

_____

41. VFR travel _____

_____

Name   Date

Directions: Check the Sunday travel section of your newspaper or the newspaper of a major city near you. Choose two advertisements and compare them by answering the following questions:

1. Who is the distributor?

    a. Ad #1 _____

    b. Ad #2 _____

2. What types of suppliers does the ad represent?

    a. Ad #1 _____

    _____

    b. Ad #2 _____

    _____

3. What type(s) of consumer does the ad target?

    a. Ad #1 _____

    _____

    b. Ad #2 _____

    _____

4. Do you think that the ad is effective? Why or why not?

    a. Ad #1 _____

    _____

    _____

    b. Ad #2 _____

    _____

    _____

Name   Date

Directions: Each destination offers a combination of characteristics that makes it unique. Choose a destination with which you are familiar.

Destination: _____

What psychographic segment(s) is likely to be attracted to your destination? (Look again at Figure 1.4 on page 12 in the textbook.) Why?

_____

_____

_____

_____

_____

_____

_____

_____

_____

_____

_____

_____

_____

_____

_____

_____

_____

_____

_____

_____

Worksheet 1.4 Travel Careers

Name _____   Date _____

Directions: Describe five skill areas needed for entry-level positions in the travel industry and why each is important.

1. Skill area: _____

   _____

   _____

2. Skill area: _____

   _____

   _____

3. Skill area: _____

   _____

   _____

4. Skill area: _____

   _____

   _____

5. Skill area: _____

   _____

   _____

Directions: List five tasks that you have performed in the past two years, and then list the skill area that each falls into. (You may want to refer to this information when you are preparing your résumé.)

6. **Task performed**   **Skill area**

   a. _____   _____

   b. _____   _____

   c. _____   _____

   d. _____   _____

   e. _____   _____

Name _____   Date _____

Directions: Match the mode of travel with the description: (a) air travel, (b) automobile travel, (c) rail transportation, or (d) ship transportation.

1. The major method of travel between continents before the twentieth century

   _____

2. The major method of transcontinental travel in North America a century ago

   _____

3. The type of travel that grew steadily more important throughout the twentieth century, becoming the mode of transportation used for most trips in the United States

   _____

4. The mode of transportation that grew steadily after World War II, influencing every aspect of the travel industry

   _____

Directions: Answer the following questions.

5. What two specific destinations would you recommend to the following types of travelers? Why?

   a. Venturer _____

   _____

   _____

   b. Centric _____

   _____

   _____

   c. Dependable _____

   _____

   _____

6. List and describe four ways to segment markets.

   a. _____

   _____

   b. _____

   _____

(continued)

c. _____

_____

d. _____

_____

7. List three main types of travel and give an example of each.

a. _____

_____

b. _____

_____

c. _____

_____

8. Explain the difference between a feature and a benefit.

_____

_____

_____

_____

Name _____ Date _____

Directions: For practice in using the Web sites of some prominent sources of information on travel and the travel industry, complete the following exercises. (If you work on your own computer, you may wish to add the Web sites mentioned in the Technology Technique worksheets to your list of "favorites" or "bookmarks" for future use.)

1. Go to *Travel Weekly*'s Web site (www.travelweekly.com) on two days. Choose one article that interests you on each day. For each article, write the title and a sentence that explains why it interests you.

   Article #1 _____

   _____

   Article #2 _____

   _____

2. Enter a travel-related topic in the Search box at *Travel Weekly*'s site. How many articles related to your topic are listed? Choose one and read it. Write its title, and summarize the article in a paragraph.

   Number of articles _____

   Title and summary of selected article _____

   _____

   _____

   _____

   _____

   _____

3. Go to the Web site of the Tourism Industry Association of America (www.tia.org), and choose one of its top stories. Write the topic of that story and one sentence explaining why it is important in today's travel climate.

   _____

   _____

   _____

4. Find and go to the Web site of either the Tourism Industries Office of the International Trade Administration at the U.S. Department of Commerce or the Bureau of Transportation Statistics of the U.S. Department of Transportation. Choose one statistic that might be valuable to you in selling travel, and write one sentence explaining why knowing this statistic might be useful.

   Statistic _____

   _____

(continued)

Usefulness _____

_____

5. Go to the Web site of *Travel Industry World Yearbook* (www.travelbigpicture.com). Choose one trend described there, and explain in a sentence how it might influence one specific aspect of travel and tourism that interests you.

Trend _____

_____

Possible influence _____

_____

6. Go to ASTA's Web site (www.astanet.com). Who is the ASTA agent nearest you? (Tip: Enter your home zip code under "Find an agent.")

_____

Name   Date

Directions: Consider the following issues. Conduct research to help you respond, and be prepared to discuss the topic in class. (Tip: Refer to the Web sites listed in the "Resources" section on page 18 of Chapter 1 of the *Travel Career Development* textbook and other resources.)

1. Check the Web sites of at least two travel and tourism organizations, and find their forecasts for the future of the travel industry. What are their projections for the growth of the industry? Do they identify any specific challenges and opportunities?

_____

_____

_____

_____

_____

_____

_____

_____

_____

_____

2. Many factors have a direct impact on the travel industry. How can changes in economic or political conditions affect a destination's tourism industry? What other factors would have a direct impact on the travel and tourism industry at a destination?

_____

_____

_____

_____

_____

_____

_____

_____

_____

_____

Name _____   Date _____

1. Amadeus _____

   _____

2. Bricks-and-clicks agency _____

   _____

3. Browser _____

   _____

4. Command interface _____

   _____

5. CRS _____

   _____

6. Database _____

   _____

7. Direct link _____

   _____

8. E-mail _____

   _____

9. Galileo _____

   _____

10. GDS _____

    _____

11. Graphical interface _____

    _____

12. Hotspot _____

    _____

13. Internet _____

    _____

(continued)

14. ISP _____

_____

15. Sabre _____

_____

16. Search engine _____

_____

17. URL _____

_____

18. WiFi _____

_____

19. Worldspan _____

_____

20. World Wide Web _____

_____

Name   Date

Directions: Circle the letter indicating the best answer to each question.

1. Which of the following statements about GDSs is true?
   a. Today's GDSs can run a host of programs.
   b. Both command and graphical interfaces are available on GDSs.
   c. Companies can gain access to a GDS in several ways.
   d. All of the above are true.

2. A direct link between a supplier's computer system and the GDS
   a. ensures that the information on the GDS about the supplier's product is up-to-date.
   b. is not useful.
   c. exists for all suppliers that participate in a GDS.
   d. has become obsolete.

3. The information on a GDS
   a. is carefully regulated by the U.S. Department of Transportation.
   b. is closely regulated by the FCC.
   c. is no longer regulated by the federal government.
   d. is regulated by ARC.

4. Which GDS is owned by several European airlines?
   a. Sabre
   b. Galileo
   c. Amadeus
   d. Worldspan

5. A computer can be linked to the Internet through
   a. phone lines or cable.
   b. DSL or a satellite.
   c. a WiFi network.
   d. any of the above.

6. What would you set up if you wanted a messaging system accessible only to people within a company?
   a. A listserv
   b. A usenet
   c. A chat room
   d. An intranet

7. What is www.thetravelinstitute.com?
   a. A protocol for browsers
   b. A bulletin board
   c. An ISP
   d. A URL

8. What are Google, Lycos, Yahoo, Go, and AltaVista?
   a. URLs
   b. Bulletin boards
   c. Search engines
   d. GDSs

(continued)

Directions: Fill in the blanks.

9. Five tasks unrelated to airline travel that a CRS can perform are

   a. _____

   b. _____

   c. _____

   d. _____

   e. _____

10. Three reasons to use e-mail are

    a. _____

    b. _____

    c. _____

11. Web sites that are likely to offer research material on travel include those hosted by

    a. _____

    b. _____

    c. _____

    d. _____

12. When using the Web for research, you should take three steps to ensure the quality of the information:

    a. _____

    b. _____

    c. _____

Name   Date

Directions: Indicate whether the following statements are true or false. If a statement is false, rewrite it to create a true statement.

1. Compared with a graphical interface, a command interface allows the user to enter information more quickly. True or false?

   _____

2. Linking information from a client database with information from an accounting system is easily done with integrated software. True or false?

   _____

3. Booking engines such as VAX VacationAccess allow travel agencies to book online more easily. True or false?

   _____

4. Dynamic packaging makes it easier for travel agencies to go online to create a travel package, book several types of travel components online, and offer clients a travel package with just a single overall price. True or false?

   _____

5. A back-office system like TRAMS's BOS handles accounting and marketing tasks. True or false?

   _____

6. Today, most GDSs are owned and operated by the leading airlines. True or false?

   _____

7. Information on the Internet must be true or it couldn't be published there. True or false?

   _____

8. The Internet is used by a lot of "lookers" who can be turned into "bookers" by enterprising travel counselors. True or false?

   _____

9. Expedia and Travelocity are leading online travel agencies. True or false?

   _____

10. Many Web sites can offer a vast array of information on the Internet for free because companies pay to advertise on Web sites. True or false?

   _____

11. A travel agency that has both a retail location and a strong Internet presence might be called a bricks-and-mortar agency. True or false?

_____

12. One important service that travel counselors can provide is to use their relationships with suppliers to verify information that clients find on the Web. True or false?

_____

Name   Date

Directions: For practice using the Web sites that are prominent sources of information about the travel industry, complete the following exercises.

1. Enter "travel technology" in the Search box at *Travel Weekly*'s Web site. Choose an article that interests you and write a one-paragraph statement of what you learned from it.

   Article _____

   _____

   _____

   _____

   _____

2. Find and go to the Web site of one of the major GDSs; then choose one article from its press releases or other information sections. Summarize the article you have chosen in a sentence or two.

   Article _____

   _____

   _____

   _____

   _____

3. Go to two search engines of your choice (such as www.yahoo.com or www.google.com), and enter a travel-related topic that interests you into the Search box of each. How would you characterize the differences in the results?

   Search engines _____

   _____

   _____

   _____

4. Use a search engine to find the Web site of *National Geographic* magazine. What are the featured stories for this month?

   _____

   _____

   _____

(continued)

5. Use your favorite search engine to find the names of three dynamic packaging tools for travel agencies.

_____

_____

_____

Name   Date

Directions: Consider the following issue. Conduct research to help you respond, and be prepared to discuss the topic in class. (Tip: Refer to the Web sites listed in the "Resources: On Technology" section on page 39 of Chapter 2 of the *Travel Career Development* textbook and other resources.)

Technology's impact on travel

Technology has changed the way the world conducts business. What are some of the ways technology has changed the travel industry? Some people predicted that the Internet would decrease the need to travel. In your opinion, has this happened? Why or why not? Write one or two paragraphs in response.

Name _____   Date _____

Directions: Define the following terms.

1. Altitude _____

   _____

2. Atlas _____

   _____

3. Climate _____

   _____

4. Consulate _____

   _____

5. Continent _____

   _____

6. Destination _____

   _____

7. Destination geography _____

   _____

8. Destination management and promotion _____

   _____

9. Duty _____

   _____

10. Duty-free port _____

   _____

11. Embassy _____

   _____

12. Equator _____

   _____

(continued)

13. Exchange rate _____

_____

14. Familiarization trip (fam trip) _____

_____

15. Geography _____

_____

16. GMT _____

_____

17. Gulf _____

_____

18. International date line _____

_____

19. Island _____

_____

20. Isthmus _____

_____

21. Latitude _____

_____

22. Leeward _____

_____

23. Longitude _____

_____

24. Mediterranean climate _____

_____

25. Metric system _____

_____

Name _____ Date _____

26. Monsoon _____

_____

27. Ocean _____

_____

28. Passport _____

_____

29. Peninsula _____

_____

30. Prime meridian _____

_____

31. River _____

_____

32. Sea _____

_____

33. Sound _____

_____

34. Strait _____

_____

35. Tourist card _____

_____

36. The Travel Institute _____

_____

37. 24-hour clock _____

_____

38. UTC _____

_____

39. VAT _____

_____

40. Visa _____

_____

41. Windward _____

_____

Name _____ Date _____

Directions: Each destination offers a combination of characteristics that makes it unique. Choose a destination with which you are familiar.

Destination _____

1. Describe the following characteristics of your destination, and explain how each adds to (or subtracts from) its popularity.

   a. Climate _____

   _____

   b. Attractions _____

   _____

   c. Costs and standard of living _____

   _____

   d. Accessibility_____

   _____

   e. Culture _____

   _____

2. What other factors make your chosen destination unique?

   _____

   _____

3. Has the appeal of your destination ever changed because of unique circumstances? Explain.

   _____

   _____

   _____

4. Describe travelers who are especially likely to be attracted to your destination. In particular, can you identify demographic and psychographic segments (as discussed in Chapter 1) that are most likely to find the destination appealing? What types of special-interest travel could it attract?

   _____

   _____

   _____

_____

Name   Date

Directions: Choose the tourist offices of two U.S. states or the NTOs of two foreign countries. Call each tourist office, request tourist literature, and then answer the following questions.

State or country #1 _____

State or country #2 _____

1. How would you evaluate the customer-service skills of the office?

   State or country #1 _____

   _____

   State or country #2 _____

   _____

2. How long did it take to receive the literature?

   State or country #1 _____

   State or country #2 _____

3. How would you rate the quality of the literature?

   State or country #1: _____

   _____

   State or country #2: _____

   _____

4. If clients wanted to visit the state or country, what five attractions would you recommend?

   State or country #1 _____

   _____

   _____

   _____

   State or country #2 _____

   _____

   _____

   _____

(continued)

5. Did the literature change your perception of the state or country? If so, how?

State or country #1 _____

_____

State or country #2 _____

_____

Name   Date

Directions: Provide the requested information.

1. List three acceptable proofs of U.S. citizenship.

   a._____

   b._____

   c._____

2. Identify four items that must accompany a completed passport application form.

   a._____

   b._____

   c._____

   d._____

3. List four types of visas.

   a._____

   b._____

   c._____

   d._____

4. What document(s) do U.S. citizens need to enter Mexico?

   _____

5. What document(s) do U.S. citizens need to enter Hawaii?

   _____

6. What document(s) do U.S. citizens need to enter China?

   _____

7. What document(s) do U.S. citizens need to enter the United Kingdom?

   _____

8. What document(s) do U.S. citizens need to enter the Bahamas?

   _____

(continued)

Directions: For each scenario, indicate the maximum worth of goods that U.S. residents would be allowed to bring with them back into the country: (a) $400, (b) $600, (c) $800, (d) $1,200, (e) $1,600, or (f) $3,200.

9. A family of four (two children, ages 3 and 12) returning from Europe

   _____

10. A couple returning from Mexico

    _____

11. A couple returning from the Bahamas

    _____

12. A couple returning from Canada

    _____

13. A single person returning from St. Thomas

    _____

Name   Date

Directions: Circle the letter indicating the best answer to each question.

1. Buying a liter of Burgundy wine in France is the equivalent of buying how much wine in the United States?
   a. A half-pint
   b. A quart
   c. A half-gallon
   d. A gallon

2. Driving the hundred or so kilometers from Madrid to Ávila in Spain is roughly equivalent to driving how many miles in the United States?
   a. 60 miles
   b. 100 miles
   c. 160 miles
   d. 212 miles

3. What kind of U.S. race is roughly equivalent to the 1,500-meter race in Athens?
   a. A 100-yard dash
   b. A one-mile race
   c. A two-mile race
   d. A marathon

4. Buying a kilogram of pasta in Palermo is roughly equivalent to buying how much in the United States?
   a. A quarter-pound
   b. A half-pound
   c. A pound
   d. Two pounds

Directions: Convert the following metric measurements to the system usually used in the United States.

5. 40 liters of petrol (gasoline) in England = _____ U.S. gallons

6. 100 grams of prosciutto in Italy = _____ ounces

7. 550 kilometers on the German autobahn = _____ miles

8. 32° Fahrenheit in Moscow, Idaho = _____ ° Celsius in Moscow, Russia

9. A sign announcing "Zona escuela 40 meters" in Mexico means that the school zone is about how many mile(s) ahead?

(continued)

Directions: Answer the following questions.

10. What recommendations would you give clients traveling abroad who ask advice about using credit cards such as American Express, Diner's Club, Visa, or MasterCard?

_____

_____

_____

_____

_____

_____

11. Would you recommend that your clients buy traveler's checks for their vacations? Why or why not?

_____

_____

_____

_____

_____

_____

Name   Date

Directions: Indicate which type of geography is reflected in each of the following statements: locational geography, physical geography, or cultural geography. (Bonus: Name the places described.)

1. Broad rivers flow from the Andes to the Atlantic across this country.

   _____

2. This physically rugged country has Pakistan on its southeastern border and Iran on its western border.

   _____

3. The practice of Hinduism is located primarily on one island of this mostly Islamic archipelago.

   _____

4. An active volcanic landscape, deep valleys, and a mountain rising from the sea to 13,000 feet characterize this U.S. island.

   _____

Directions: Circle the letter indicating the best answer to each question.

5. You can snow-ski in Hawaii primarily because of what characteristic on one island?
   a. Its latitude
   b. Its longitude
   c. Its altitude
   d. The leeward side

6. Which attribute of a location tells you the least about its climate?
   a. Latitude
   b. Longitude
   c. Altitude
   d. Proximity to water

7. Which of these topics should you be most inclined to discuss with your client?
   a. What the weather will be like on the trip
   b. What the climate is like at the destination

8. The prime meridian is also called
   a. the equator.
   b. the Greenwich mean line.
   c. the international date line.
   d. 180° north or south.

(continued)

9. A duty-free port means that
    a. items bought are not taxed but must be used solely for that port.
    b. items bought are not taxed coming into the port but are taxed going out.
    c. items bought are not taxed coming into or out of the port but may be taxed when brought into another country.
    d. items bought are not taxed coming into or out of the port, nor can they be taxed when entering another country.

Directions: Answer the following questions. (For help, you can refer to the atlas at the end of the textbook.)

10. What two continents are attached to each other by an isthmus that also separates the world's two largest oceans?

_____

11. What two continents meet at a rather small land bridge that also separates two of the world's most important seas?

_____

12. Russia and Turkey are said by most geographers to be the only countries that have part of their land on two continents. What are these two continents?

_____

13. The Western Hemisphere consists of which two continents?

_____

14. Only scientists and visitors (all of whom eventually go home) live on this continent.

_____

15. Flying from Seattle to Honolulu takes you over this ocean.

_____

16. Flying from Australia to Africa takes you over this ocean.

_____

Directions: Indicate whether the following statements are true or false. If a statement is false, rewrite it to create a true statement.

17. A peninsula is a narrow body of land joining two larger bodies of land. True or false?

_____

18. A legend, or key, on a map explains the symbols that are used on the map. True or false?

_____

Name   Date

19. The higher the altitude, the warmer the climate is likely to be. True or false?

20. The Gulf Stream is a major warm ocean current that flows north from the Caribbean area. True or false?

21. Longitudes are distances measured north or south of the equator. True or false?

22. Areas with a Mediterranean climate have warm, dry summers and mild, wet winters. True or false?

Directions: Convert the following times from the 24-hour clock to A.M./P.M. format.

23. 1359 _____

25. 0600 _____

24. 2100 _____

26. 1502 _____

Directions: Convert the following to times on the 24-hour clock.

27. 3:25 P.M. _____

29. 8:58 P.M. _____

28. 11:50 A.M. _____

30. 10:05 P.M. _____

Directions: Answer the following questions.

31. If it is 0700 in Chicago, Illinois (GMT -6), what time is it in Honolulu, Hawaii (GMT -10)? Give the answer both according to the 24-hour clock and in A.M./P.M. format.

32. If it is 1400 in Rome, Italy (GMT +1), what time is it in Los Angeles, California (GMT -8)? Give the answer both according to the 24-hour clock and in A.M./P.M. format.

33. If a flight departs London at 1400 (GMT) and arrives in Chicago at 1600 (GMT -6), how long is the flight?

34. If a flight departs Los Angeles at 1600 (GMT -8) and arrives in London at 1000 (GMT) the next day, how long is the flight?

(continued)

35. A direct flight from California to Australia takes between 15 and 20 hours. But a schedule would show that a client who departs on January 1 would arrive on January 3. Explain why. (And explain what would happen if that client's birthday was on January 2.)

_____

36. On a flight from Fiji to Tahiti, a client might depart on January 1 and arrive on December 31. Explain why.

_____

37. Where in your area would you send your clients to get a passport?

_____

38. When and why would you advise clients to take a transformer on their journey?

_____

39. When and why would you advise clients to take an adapter on their journey?

_____

40. What might you advise clients about the VAT in some countries?

_____

Name _____   Date _____

Directions: Use the Web to answer the following questions.

1. If you wanted to give a client an idea of how large France is, what state in the United States would you compare it to? (Tip: Find the answer by going to the "World Factbook" section on the CIA's Web site.)

_____

2. Choose a major European country. In what U.S. cities does this country have tourist offices? (Tip: Go to the worldwide tourism office finder at www.towd.com.).

_____

_____

3. Go to the Web to answer the following: When is the best time in terms of climate to go to Nigeria and why?

_____

_____

_____

4. What are the temperature and precipitation today in Paris, France? (Tip: Go to the weather channel at www.weather.com unless you know another Web site.)

_____

5. What is the current time in Newfoundland? (Tip: Go to www.worldtimeserver.com.) How many hours is Newfoundland ahead of your time zone?

_____

Directions: For practice in using the Web to find out more about specific destinations, complete the following exercises.

6. Go to the Web site for DK Publishing (www.dk.com), and see if you can navigate through the site to find a list of their Eyewitness Travel Guides. List three of your favorite destinations covered by this guidebook series.

    a. _____

    b. _____

    c. _____

7. Go to the Web site for Fodor's guidebooks, and pick a city. Find a restaurant, and read how Fodor's reviewers rate it or what fellow travelers say about it under "rants and raves." Summarize what you found in a few sentences.

_____

_____

Directions: Use a Web site such as www.xe.com to obtain the following information for clients. Answers may differ slightly from one day to another.

8. The Centre Ville Etoile Hotel in Paris is listed at 110 euros. What is the price in U.S. dollars?

   _____

9. A half-day tour of a volcano and rain forest outside of San José costs 17,000 Costa Rican colones. How much will that cost your clients in U.S. dollars?

   _____

10. The bullet train from Tokyo to Osaka is listed at 15,500 yen. How much will that cost in U.S. dollars?

    _____

11. Your client cashes in a $100 traveler's check in Canada. How many Canadian dollars will he receive?

    _____

12. Your clients cash in a $100 traveler's check to pay for a dinner bill that comes to 500 pesos in Mexico City. How many pesos will you receive in change?

    _____

Name   Date

Directions: Consider the following issue. Conduct research to help you respond, and be prepared to discuss the topic in class. (Tip: Refer to the Web sites listed in the "Resources: On Destinations and International Travel" section on page 70 of Chapter 3 of the *Travel Career Development* textbook and other resources.)

Sustainable development and management of tourism

Tourism can bring many positive changes to a community, such as jobs, economic growth, and a higher standard of living, but tourism also can have harmful effects. What are some of the negative impacts that tourism can have that communities or countries need to guard against?

Find an example of an area that has experienced negative effects due to tourism. Write a two-paragraph essay that describes these effects and addresses the following questions: Have people in the area taken steps to improve the situation? If so, what have they done? If not, what can be done? What resources do they have available to help them devise a plan?

_____

_____

_____

_____

_____

_____

_____

_____

_____

_____

_____

_____

_____

_____

_____

_____

_____

_____

Name _____   Date _____

Directions: Define the following terms.

1. Airline Deregulation Act _____

   _____

2. ARC _____

   _____

3. ATA _____

   _____

4. APEX fare _____

   _____

5. Arrival tax _____

   _____

6. Boarding pass _____

   _____

7. Buffer zone _____

   _____

8. Bulkhead _____

   _____

9. Bumped _____

   _____

10. Business class _____

    _____

11. Charter _____

    _____

12. Circle trip _____

    _____

(continued)

13. Civil aviation _____

_____

14. Classes of service _____

_____

15. Coach _____ _____

_____

16. Code-sharing agreements _____

_____

17. Commuter airline _____

_____

18. Configuration _____

_____

19. Confirmed _____

_____

20. Connecting flight _____

_____

21. Connection _____

_____

22. Consolidator _____

_____

23. Construction principles _____

_____

24. Denied boarding compensation _____

_____

25. Departure tax _____

_____

Name _____ Date _____

26. Direct flight _____

_____

27. Discount fare _____

_____

28. Domestic air travel _____

_____

29. Economy class _____

_____

30. Electronic ticket _____

_____

31. Excess baggage charge _____

_____

32. Executive class _____

_____

33. FAA _____

_____

34. First class _____

_____

35. Frequent-flyer plan _____

_____

36. Gateway _____

_____

37. HIP _____

_____

38. Hub-and-spoke system _____

_____

(continued)

39. IATA _____

_____

40. IATAN _____

_____

41. Interline agreement _____

_____

42. Joint fare _____

_____

43. Mileage system _____

_____

44. MPM _____

_____

45. Nonstop flight _____

_____

46. No-show _____

_____

47. NTSB _____

_____

48. NUC _____

_____

49. One-way trip _____

_____

50. Open-jaw trip _____

_____

51. Open-skies policy _____

_____

Name   Date

52. Overbook _____

_____

53. Oversold _____

_____

54. Paper ticket _____

_____

55. Passenger load factor _____

_____

56. PFC _____

_____

57. Pitch _____

_____

58. PNR _____

_____

59. Point-to-point fare _____

_____

60. Promotional fare _____

_____

61. Rate desk _____

_____

62. Record locator number _____

_____

63. Round-trip _____

_____

64. Routing system _____

_____

65. Scheduled service _____

_____

66. Seat width _____

_____

67. Security fee _____

_____

68. Segment tax _____

_____

69. Standard ticket _____

_____

70. Standby _____

_____

71. Stop _____

_____

72. Stopover _____

_____

73. STP _____

_____

74. Through fare _____

_____

75. Through flight _____

_____

76. TSA _____

_____

77. U.S. ticket tax _____

_____

Name   Date

78. Waitlisted _____

_____

79. Yield _____

_____

80. Yield management system _____

_____

Name _____   Date _____

Directions: Answer the following questions in the space provided.

1. What were the effects of the Airline Deregulation Act of 1978 on each of the following?

   a. Airlines _____

   _____

   b. Travel counselors _____

   _____

   c. Consumers _____

   _____

2. Name one advantage and one disadvantage of the hub-and-spoke system from the viewpoint of the airlines.

   _____

   _____

3. Name one advantage and one disadvantage of the hub-and-spoke system for travelers.

   _____

   _____

4. What are some key benefits offered by airline-sponsored members-only lounges?

   _____

   _____

5. Why should travel counselors be aware of code sharing by airlines, and what should they do about it?

   _____

   _____

   _____

6. What should travel counselors advise clients about security and check-in times?

   _____

   _____

   _____

(continued)

Directions: Circle the letter indicating the best answer to each question.

7. The primary function of the FAA is
   a. to ensure that the airline system is regulated financially.
   b. to settle strikes and make certain that the airlines keep flying.
   c. to enforce rules regarding passenger safety.
   d. to see that travelers are not overcharged for tickets.

8. The FAA is a division of the
   a. NTSB.
   b. ARC.
   c. CAB.
   d. DOT.

9. What airline organization do travel agencies deal with most frequently?
   a. FAA
   b. ARC
   c. ATA
   d. DOT

Name _____   Date _____

Directions: Fill in the airport and airline codes.

Airport	Code
1. Boston, MA	
2. Detroit, MI/Wayne County	
3. Dallas, TX	
4. Kansas City, MO	
5. Los Angeles, CA/Burbank	
6. St. Louis, MO	
7. Pittsburgh, PA	
8. Salt Lake City, UT	
9. Denver, CO	
10. Atlanta, GA	
11. Minneapolis, MN	
12. Chicago, IL/Midway	
13. Cleveland, OH	
14. Orlando, FL/International	
15. Mexico City, MX	
16. Washington, DC/Dulles	
17. Richmond, VA	
18. Charleston, SC	
19. Phoenix, AZ	
20. Seattle, WA	
21. Milwaukee, WI	
22. Ottawa, Ont.	
23. Indianapolis, IN	
24. Little Rock, AR	

(continued)

Airport	Code
25. Nassau, Bahamas	
26. New Orleans, LA	

Airline	Code
27. United Airlines	
28. US Airways	
29. American Airlines	
30. Delta Airlines	
31. America West Airlines	
32. Hawaiian Airlines	
33. Continental Airlines	
34. Southwest Airlines	

Name _____   Date _____

Directions: List the major gateway city for each country and the major airport code(s) for that city.

Country	Major gateway city	Major airport code
1. England	_____	_____
	_____	_____
2. France	_____	_____
	_____	_____
3. India	_____	_____
4. Egypt	_____	_____
5. Netherlands	_____	_____
6. Austria	_____	_____
7. Italy	_____	_____
	_____	_____
8. Spain	_____	_____
9. Ireland	_____	_____
	_____	_____
10. Argentina	_____	_____
11. China	_____	_____
12. Australia	_____	_____
13. Japan	_____	_____
14. Russia	_____	_____
15. Costa Rica	_____	_____

Directions: Name the flag carriers of the countries listed and give their two-letter codes.

Country	Flag carrier (airline)	Airline code
16. Israel	_____	_____
17. Mexico	_____	_____
18. Germany	_____	_____

(continued)

Country	Flag carrier (airline)	Airline code
19. Morocco		
20. New Zealand		
21. Ecuador		
22. Korea		
23. Denmark/Norway/Sweden		
24. Brazil		
25. Portugal		
26. Greece		
27. Jordan		
28. Iceland		
29. Poland		
30. Australia		

Name   Date

Directions: Indicate whether the following statements are true or false. If a statement is false, rewrite it to create a true statement.

1. On a connecting flight the passenger makes one stop between his or her origin and destination. True or false?

   _____

2. Passengers almost always prefer nonstop flights to connections. True or false?

   _____

3. In general, a direct flight is one on which the aircraft may make one or more stops but passengers do not have to change planes. True or false?

   _____

4. On some direct flights there is a change of plane that requires passengers to switch from one aircraft to another. Truc or false?

   _____

5. A through flight is a nonstop flight. True or false?

   _____

Directions: Identify each of the following itineraries as a one-way trip, a round trip, a circle trip, or an open-jaw trip.

6. New York to Orlando on Delta   _____
   Orlando to New York on Delta

7. Atlanta to Houston on Delta   _____
   Houston to Atlanta on American

8. Chicago to Las Vegas on America West   _____
   Las Vegas to Los Angeles on America West
   Los Angeles to Phoenix on America West
   Phoenix to Chicago on America West

9. Boston to Chicago to Los Angeles on   _____
   American on the same day with a 90-minute
   layover in Chicago

10. Chicago to Los Angeles on American   _____
    Surface to San Francisco
    San Francisco to Chicago on American

11. New York to London   _____
    London to Boston

Name   Date

Directions: Today is January 1. An airfare has been announced by International Airways for $399 (slightly higher on Friday to Sunday) round-trip from your major city to Rome on direct flights. The fare has a 7-day minimum/30-day maximum stay. It must be booked 7 days in advance, and it must be ticketed within 1 day of booking. A $100 cancellation or change fee applies. The fare sale ends January 15 and is for travel from January 1 to March 31. Blackout dates are February 12 and March 17. The number of seats is capacity controlled, and interlining is not allowed.

Answer "Yes" or "No" to the following questions. If the answer is "No," describe what you would do or say to the client to make him or her eligible for the fare and to make the sale.

1. A client calls today and wants to travel from February 13 to March 13. Will she be eligible for the fare?

_____

2. A client calls today and wants to travel from January 17 to February 17. Will she be eligible for the fare?

_____

3. A client calls on January 17 and wants to travel from March 18 to March 30. Will she be eligible for the fare?

_____

4. A client calls on January 10 and wants to travel from January 15 to January 31. Will she be eligible for the fare?

_____

5. A client calls today and says she must travel on January 31 and return on February 14. She is told that the seats are sold out but that she can travel on the same flights on the same days for $599. She insists that she be given the $399 fare because it is obvious that seats are available. Will she prevail in her argument?

_____

6. A client calls today and wants to travel on March 4 and return March 11. He wants to book a connection through Paris on the return (the airline does have a connecting schedule) in order to purchase something at the duty-free shop in the Paris airport. Will he be eligible for the fare?

_____

7. Universal Airlines is offering the same fare as International Airways and has flight times on the return that are better for one particular client. Will he be eligible for the fare if he takes International on the outbound flight and Universal on the return?

_____

8. A client calls on January 10 and makes a reservation to travel between March 1 and March 14 and says that he will come in the next day with his payment for ticketing. The next day he comes in and decides to change his return from March 14 to March 15. Will he be eligible for the fare?

_____

(continued)

9. A client calls on January 10 and wants to travel from February 28 to March 17. By what day must he be ticketed to be eligible for the fare?

_____

10. A client calls on January 15 and wants to travel between January 22 and January 29. By what day must he be ticketed to be eligible for the fare?

_____

Name   Date

Directions: Answer the following questions.

1. What are three benefits of traveling first class?

   a. _____

   b. _____

   c. _____

2. What is one circumstance in which you would waitlist a client on a flight?

   _____

3. What is one reason that many clients prefer ticketless travel?

   _____

4. What is one reason that some clients prefer a paper ticket to an electronic ticket?

   _____

5. What is your preferred place to sit on a plane and why?

   _____

6. Passengers holding ticket/boarding passes are automatically guaranteed a seat on their flight no matter when they arrive at the gate. True or false?

   _____

7. Airlines must provide compensation for clients involuntarily bumped from flights. True or false?

   _____

8. It is illegal for airlines to overbook flights. True or false?

   _____

9. Business or executive classes range somewhere between first class and coach in amenities. True or false?

   _____

10. Special meals on a flight need to be ordered at least 12 to 24 hours in advance. True or false?

    _____

11. What is the difference between a wide-bodied and a narrow-bodied plane?

    _____

(continued)

12. If you were a travel counselor or airline reservations agent helping a first-time flyer select a seat, how would you summarize the pros and cons of these seating options?

    a. Over the wings

    _____

    _____

    _____

    b. Emergency exit rows

    _____

    _____

    _____

    c. Middle rows

    _____

    _____

    _____

    d. Aisle seats

    _____

    _____

    _____

    e. Bulkhead seats

    _____

    _____

    _____

13. What is an airline rate desk? What service does it offer travel counselors?

    _____

    _____

    _____

Name   Date

14. What is the major advantage to travelers having their international air tickets booked through a consolidator rather than directly through an airline?

_____

_____

_____

15. What are three disadvantages to booking international air tickets through a consolidator?

 a. _____

 b. _____

 c. _____

16. What are two major advantages to travelers in taking a charter?

 a. Advantages _____

 b. Disadvantages _____

Directions: Circle the letter indicating the best answer to each question.

17. On international flights, the charge for an infant not occupying a seat is generally
 a. half of the adult fare, regardless of the discount on the fare.
 b. one-quarter of the adult fare.
 c. 10 percent of the adult fare.
 d. nothing; infants fly free.

18. The standard term on international flights for what is called coach class on U.S. domestic flights is
 a. economy.
 b. second.
 c. open.
 d. steerage.

Name _____   Date _____

Directions: Choose a major U.S. city pair for a round-trip itinerary. (You might choose a destination that you or someone you know is actually planning to visit.) Find the best round-trip fare available between those two cities regardless of dates by going to each of the following: (a) either Travelocity or Expedia, (b) Orbitz, and (c) a major U.S. airline's Web site.

Destination _____

1. What airfares did you find?

   a. _____

   b. _____

   c. _____

2. When searching for the fares, what difference did you encounter among the Web sites?

   _____

   _____

   _____

3. Which site would be your first choice if you were to use one of them for your next trip?

   _____

Directions: Practice finding travel-related information on the Web by completing the following exercises.

4. Summarize an item of "late-breaking news" on ARC's Web site in a sentence or two.

   _____

   _____

   _____

5. List three topics and their section numbers from the "Industry Agent's Handbook" at ARC's Web site.

   a. _____

   b. _____

   c. _____

6. What are the on-time statistics for airlines at the largest airport close to you? (Tip: Go to www.faa.gov.)

   _____

(continued)

7. List the current threat level by accessing www.dhs.gov. Comment on one of the security tips given at www.tsa.gov.

   _____

   _____

   _____

8. Choose one topic that interests you at the Air Transport Association's Web site (www.airlines.org), and summarize it in a sentence or two.

   _____

   _____

   _____

   _____

Directions: Complete the following exercises for practice in finding information about international travel at prominent Web sites.

9. Choose a major international city and a U.S. city for a round-trip itinerary. Check airfares for three months from now by going to three Web sites: (a) either Travelocity or Expedia, (b) Orbitz, and (c) a major U.S. airline's Web site.

Itinerary _____

   a. _____

   b. _____

   c. _____

10. Go to a consolidator's Web site (try www.airlineconsolidator.com) for the same round-trip itinerary that you checked in the previous exercise. Compare the fares and the restrictions on scheduling or other rules described on the consolidator's Web site with those you found in the previous question.

    _____

    _____

11. Go to the Web site for the U.S. State Department (www.travel.state.gov). How many "Current Travel Warnings" and "Current Public Announcements" are posted today?

    _____

    _____

Name   Date

12. Choose one region of the world. Then go to the Web site of the Centers for Disease Control and Prevention to determine the special precautions that a client must take when traveling to that region. Summarize your findings.

_____

_____

_____

Name   Date

Directions: Consider the following concepts and issues. Conduct research to help you respond, and be prepared to discuss the topic in class. (Tip: Refer to the Web sites listed in the "Resources: On Air Travel" section on page 115 of Chapter 4 of the *Travel Career Development* textbook and other resources.)

New business model: low-cost carriers

New low-cost airlines are establishing and providing air service in many areas across the globe. Many of these new carriers are actually making a profit at a time when the major long-standing airlines are financially strapped and losing money. How is this possible? What do the low-cost carriers do that the major airlines have been unable to do? Find a few of their Web sites; they are happy to tell the public what they are doing right.

Write a paragraph or two that lists their strategies and describes how they differ from the major airlines.

_____

_____

_____

_____

_____

_____

_____

_____

_____

_____

_____

_____

_____

_____

_____

_____

_____

_____

Name _____   Date _____

Directions: Define the following terms.

1. AAA _____

_____

2. Acela Express _____

_____

3. ALI _____

_____

4. Amtrak _____

_____

5. BritRail pass _____

_____

6. Bullet train _____

_____

7. Canrailpass _____

_____

8. CDW _____

_____

9. Couchette _____

_____

10. ELI _____

_____

11. Eurailpass _____

_____

12. Eurostar _____

_____

(continued)

13. Excursion fare _____

_____

14. Explore America fare _____

_____

15. IDP _____

_____

16. LDW _____

_____

17. Motorcoach _____

_____

18. PAI _____

_____

19. Rail Europe _____

_____

20. Rail pass _____

_____

21. Specialty train _____

_____

22. Transfers _____

_____

23. USA Rail pass _____

_____

24. VIA Rail _____

_____

Name   Date

Directions: Refer to the schedule for the Metroliner/Acela Express on page 243 to answer the following questions.

1. At what time does train #2153 depart Boston's Back Bay Station? How long is the trip from this station to New York?

2. What is the final destination of train #2153? How long is the trip from New York to this final destination?

3. What time does train #2153 stop in Philadelphia?

4. What is the earliest departure time for a passenger wishing to travel on a Sunday from New York to Washington?

5. Which airport is served by the Metroliner/Acela Express?

Directions: Refer to the Eurostar fare and schedule tables on pages 244–246 to answer the following questions.

6. What is the lowest round-trip adult fare from London to Paris (excluding wheelchair adult fares)? What is the major restriction on this fare?

7. When is the earliest that a traveler can arrive in Paris on a Sunday?

Directions: Refer to the Thomas Cook Rail Schedule on page 247 to answer the following questions.

8. From which station in Paris do TGV trains depart?

9. When does the TGV that departs from Paris at 0712 arrive in Lausanne?

10. How would you respond to a client who wants to know how far it is by train between Milano and Firenze?

(continued)

11. Are there any direct trains from Paris to Lyon? If so, when does the first one depart?

_____

Directions: Answer each of the following questions.

12. What is the key element that differentiates each of the following rail passes from other passes offered for the Eurail network?

    a. Eurailpass   _____

    _____

    b. Eurailpass Flexi   _____

    _____

    c. Eurailpass Saver   _____

    _____

    d. Eurailpass Youth   _____

    _____

    e. Eurail Selectpass   _____

    _____

13. Eurailpasses are valid for trips on ferries between what sets of countries?

_____

14. What is one major difference between the BritRail pass system and Eurailpass?

_____

Name _____ Date _____

Directions: Select a pick-up city and a date, a different drop-city and a date two weeks later, and a car type. Call two car rental companies (or go to their Web sites). Compare them by completing the following form; then determine which company you would recommend to a client based on this research.

Rental dates   From _____ To _____

Type of car _____

Pick-up location _____

Drop-off location _____

	Car rental #1	**Car rental #2**
Weekly rate	_____	_____
Drop-off charge	_____	_____
Free miles (if any)	_____	_____
Extra driver charge (if applicable)	_____	_____
Other costs	_____	_____
Total cost	_____	_____

Recommendation to client and explanation

_____

_____

_____

_____

_____

_____

_____

_____

_____

_____

Name   Date

Directions: Indicate whether the following statements are true or false. If a statement is false, rewrite it to create a true statement.

1. Amtrak trains offer sleeping accommodations on all routes. True or false?

   _____

2. Most trains in Europe offer only one class of service. True or false?

   _____

3. Eurailpasses can be purchased at any train station in Europe. True or false?

   _____

4. Most car renters need to pay for damage and collision insurance at the time of rental. True or false?

   _____

5. Eurostar operates under the Irish Sea uniting England and Ireland. True or false?

   _____

6. Rail passes by themselves do not guarantee a seat. True or false?

   _____

Directions: Provide the information requested.

7. Name three advantages of traveling by rail rather than car.

   a. _____

   b. _____

   c. _____

8. Name three advantages of traveling by car rather than rail.

   a. _____

   b. _____

   c. _____

(continued)

9. Name five ways in which full-service car rental companies try to give better service than their counterparts.

    a. _____

    b. _____

    c. _____

    d. _____

    e. _____

10. Identify four differences between renting a car in a foreign country and renting one in the United States.

    a. _____

    b. _____

    c. _____

    d. _____

Directions: For each train, identify the continent on which it travels: Africa, Asia, Australia, Europe, North America, or South America.

11. *The Copper Canyon* _____

12. *The Orient Express* _____

13. *The Palace on Wheels* _____

14. *The Blue Train* _____

15. *The Cascades* _____

16. The TGV _____

Name   Date

Directions: Refer to the Web sites listed in the "Resources: On Ground Transportation" section on page 145 of Chapter 5 in the *Travel Career Development* textbook to find the information to handle the following scenarios.

1. Abel Adams is a budget traveler who is arriving in London on July 1. He is staying in the city for four nights and then wants to travel by rail throughout all of England, seeing as much as he can of the country and the countryside. He will depart for home on July 27. Using the BritRail Web site, decide which pass would you recommend and why?

    _____

2. Betsy Baker is arriving in Edinburgh on August 25. She will stay for one week, attending events at the Edinburgh Festival, and then would like to explore Scotland by train for two weeks, traveling every other day.

    a. Which rail pass would you recommend, and why?

    _____

    b. Can Betsy take a train to Glasgow airport? Explain.

    _____

3. Upon arriving at London/Heathrow airport, Abel Adams wants to take a train into downtown London.

    a. What is the name of the train?   _____

    b. How long will it take?   _____

    c. How much does a first-class ticket cost? _____

4. What Web site will you consult for detailed up-to-the-minute train times for Abel and Betsy?

    _____

5. Cornell Corman and David Donaldson want to have a five-day stay in Paris at the start of their trip and a five-day stay in Rome at the end of their trip. They'll be away from June 1 through June 30. In between they wish to travel by train to as many locales and countries in Europe as time allows. What rail pass will you recommend to them?

    _____

6. Ed Eagleton is going to spend one week each in Paris, Berlin, Rome, Florence, Zurich, and Madrid to study the architecture. He would like to travel by first-class train between cities. (He will fly into Paris and return home from Madrid.) Which pass will you recommend to him, and why?

    _____

7. Frances and Frank are a retired couple (in their sixties) who want to travel throughout France for a month, seeing Paris, Strasbourg, Lyon, Nice, Marseille, Bordeaux, and Nantes. What pass will you recommend for them?

    _____

(continued)

Directions: Use Web sites to complete the following exercises.

8. Compare the one-day rates for a standard (full-size) car at New York/LaGuardia airport for the first Tuesday in August offered by Hertz and Budget car rental companies.

   a. Hertz   _____

   b. Budget   _____

9. Compare the one-day rates for a standard (full-size) car at Orlando airport for the first Tuesday in November offered by Avis and Alamo car rental companies.

   a. Avis   _____

   b. Alamo   _____

Name   Date

Directions: Consider the following concepts and issues. Conduct research to help you respond, and be prepared to discuss the topic in class. (Tip: Refer to the Web sites listed in the "Resources: On Ground Transportation" section on page 145 of Chapter 5 of the *Travel Career Development* textbook and other resources.)

The Future of Passenger Rail in the United States

Americans love their cars. The passenger rail service in the United States, although improving, cannot compare with the efficient rail systems in other parts of the world. Some Americans think that this is about to change. There has been an increase in light-rail systems across the nation, and many cities are considering proposals for inter-city commuter rails. What do you think? Will Americans become less dependent on their cars and turn to the rails? List the advantages and disadvantages of increased development of the passenger rail system in the United States.

_____

_____

_____

_____

_____

_____

_____

_____

_____

_____

_____

_____

_____

_____

_____

_____

_____

_____

Name _____   Date _____

Directions: Define the following terms.

1. Adjoining rooms _____
   _____

2. AH&LA _____
   _____

3. Airport hotel _____
   _____

4. All-inclusive _____
   _____

5. All-suite _____
   _____

6. AP _____
   _____

7. B&B _____
   _____

8. BP _____
   _____

9. Chain _____
   _____

10. Commercial hotel _____
    _____

11. Concierge _____
    _____

12. Connecting rooms _____
    _____

(continued)

13. Convention hotel _____

_____

14. Convention rate _____

_____

15. Corporate rate _____

_____

16. CP _____

_____

17. Demi-pension _____

_____

18. Dine-around plan _____

_____

19. EP _____

_____

20. Extended-stay hotel _____

_____

21. Franchise company _____

_____

22. Frequent-guest program _____

_____

23. Full board _____

_____

24. Group rate _____

_____

25. Guaranteed for late arrival _____

_____

Name _____ Date _____

26. Hold time _____

_____

27. Hotel consolidator _____

_____

28. Hotel representative firm _____

_____

29. Inn _____

_____

30. Management contract _____

_____

31. MAP _____

_____

32. Membership organization _____

_____

33. Minshuku _____

_____

34. Motel _____

_____

35. Motor inn _____

_____

36. Negotiated corporate rate _____

_____

37. Net rate _____

_____

38. Occupancy rate _____

_____

(continued)

39. Parador _____

_____

40. Pension _____

_____

41. Pousada _____

_____

42. Rack rate _____

_____

43. Rep firm _____

_____

44. Resort _____

_____

45. ROH rate _____

_____

46. Ryokan _____

_____

47. Spa _____

_____

48. Walking the guest _____

_____

49. Youth hostel _____

_____

Name _____ Date _____

Directions: For the each of the following kinds of accommodations, briefly describe its distinguishing features and the types of travelers that it best suits.

	Features	**Types of travelers**
1. Motel		
2. Commercial hotel		
3. Convention hotel		
4. Airport hotel		
5. All-suite		
6. Resort		
7. Spa		
8. All-inclusive		
9. Bed-and-breakfast		
10. Inn		
11. Youth hostel		

(continued)

Directions: For each type of accommodation, indicate the country with which it is most often associated.

12. Gasthaus _____   a. Africa

13. Minshukus _____   b. France

14. B&B _____   c. Germany

15. Motel _____   d. India

16. Pension _____   e. Japan

17. Pousada _____   f. Portugal

18. Parador _____   g. Spain

19. Rondavel _____   h. United Kingdom

20. Ryokan _____   i. United States

Directions: Match the meal plan in the right column with the correct description in the left column.

21. No meals at all _____   a. AP

22. Small breakfast _____   b. BP

23. Full American breakfast _____   c. CP

24. Two meals a day _____   d. EP

25. Three meals a day _____   e. MAP

Directions: Indicate which meal plan is most likely to be found at each hotel described at the left. (There are many exceptions to these answers; choose the most likely meal plan.)

26. Caribbean resort _____   a. AP

27. Standard first-class _____   b. BP
    hotel in the United States
                                                   c. CP
28. A B&B _____
                                                   d. EP
29. Secluded resort _____
    or ranch-resort   e. MAP

30. Small hotel or pension _____
    in Italy, Spain, or France

Name _____ Date _____

Directions: Using the page from the *Official Hotel Guide* on page 248, compare the Hyatt Regency Aruba Resort & Casino and the Holiday Inn Aruba Beach Resort & Casino.

	Hyatt	**Holiday Inn**
1. How many rooms are in the hotel?	_____	_____
2. How many miles is it from the airport?	_____	_____
3. What credit cards are accepted?	_____	_____
4. What is the hotel's classification?	_____	_____
5. When was the hotel built?	_____	_____
6. Does it have a beach?	_____	_____

7. At which hotel would you prefer to stay? Why?

_____

_____

_____

8. Which would you recommend to a honeymoon couple? Why?

_____

_____

_____

9. Which would you recommend to a young couple looking for lots of activity? Why?

_____

_____

_____

10. Which would you book for a family of four (with two children 12 and 7)? Why?

_____

_____

_____

Name _____ Date _____

Directions: Answer the following questions.

1. What are two advantages of lodgings that are part of a chain?

   a. _____

   b. _____

2. What are five ways of segmenting the accommodations market?

   a. _____

   b. _____

   c. _____

   d. _____

   e. _____

3. What are five characteristics that affect the price of a hotel room?

   a. _____

   b. _____

   c. _____

   d. _____

   e. _____

4. What is the responsibility of a hotel if it is oversold and a room is not available for someone with a guaranteed reservation?

   _____

   _____

5. What are the three major hotel reference guides, and what kinds of information does each provide?

   a. _____

   _____

   b. _____

   _____

   c. _____

   _____

Name   Date

Directions: Go to the Web site for the *Hotel & Travel Index* at www.htihotelink.com, and find the list of hotels within Chicago (not the surrounding area).

1. How large a convention could the Embassy Suites hotel on Columbus Drive accommodate for meetings?

   _____

2. Does the hotel have Internet service?

   _____

3. Find the listings for Whitehall Hotel and W Chicago City Center.

   a. What are their addresses?

   _____

   _____

   b. Which is closer to McCormick Place?

   _____

   c. How did you determine your answer?

   _____

Directions: Go to the STAR Service at www.starserviceonline.com.

4. What hotel is featured in the "Review of the Month"?

   _____

5. What type of client might be ideal for this hotel?

   _____

6. Would it be a good choice for a couple who want an intimate, secluded atmosphere? Why or why not?

   _____

7. Would it be a good choice for a family with three children? Why or why not?

   _____

(continued)

Directions: Examine the following Web sites:

www.travelocity.com

www.expedia.com

www.travelweb.com

www.all-hotels.com

www.localhotels.com

www.experienceispa.com

8. As a travel counselor, would you be most likely to use www.travelocity.com, www.expedia.com, or www.travelweb.com to book a hotel? Why?

    _____

    _____

    _____

    _____

9. How might you use www.all-hotels.com and www.localhotels.com as a travel counselor?

    _____

    _____

    _____

    _____

10. At www.experienceispa.com, find and list the seven general types of spas.

    _____

    _____

    _____

    _____

11. Would you use www.experienceispa.com as a travel counselor? Why or why not?

    _____

    _____

    _____

    _____

Name   Date

Directions: Consider the following concepts and issues. Conduct research to help you respond, and be prepared to discuss the topic in class. (Tip: Refer to the Web sites listed in the "Resources: On Accommodations" section on page 171 of Chapter 6 of the *Travel Career Development* textbook and other resources.)

Hotel Classifications

Choosing the right hotel for each client is critical to the customers' satisfaction of their travel experience. It can be a challenge to assess the quality of hotels without knowing the property and without an official (government) classification system in the United States.

Be prepared to discuss the advantages and disadvantages of an official hotel rating system.

Using resources written by individuals who have personally visited and inspected the property is valuable but subject to the writer's taste and point of view. The *Hotel & Travel Index* attempts to be an objective third-party reviewer by classifying hotels in 10 categories based on each property's features. However, it is important to know that *Hotel & Travel Index* does not conduct site (personal) inspections of each property in order to classify them. Equipped with this knowledge, travel professionals should check several sources to verify the quality of accommodations.

1. List several of these sources:

   _____

   _____

   _____

   _____

   _____

   _____

   _____

2. Match the descriptions to the *Hotel & Travel Index*'s classification.

   a. no-frills budget property   1. Superior Deluxe   _____

   b. full-service hotel standard   2. Moderate Tourist Class   _____

   c. mid-market economy   3. First Class   _____

   d. exclusive, highest quality   4. Superior Tourist Class   _____

   e. comfortable, limited public areas 5. Moderate First Class   _____

Name _____ Date _____

Directions: Define the following terms.

1. Aft _____

   _____

2. Bareboat charter _____

   _____

3. Berth _____

   _____

4. Bow _____

   _____

5. Cabin _____

   _____

6. CLIA _____

   _____

7. Country of registry _____

   _____

8. Cruise ship _____

   _____

9. Deck plan _____

   _____

10. Embarkation point _____

    _____

11. Expedition _____

    _____

12. Ferry _____

    _____

(continued)

13. Fly/cruise _____

_____

14. Fore _____

_____

15. Freighter _____

_____

16. Green sheet _____

_____

17. GRT _____

_____

18. Guaranteed rate _____

_____

19. Guaranteed share rate _____

_____

20. Hotel manager _____

_____

21. Knot _____

_____

22. Megaship _____

_____

23. Option date _____

_____

24. Pitch _____

_____

25. Port charges _____

_____

Name _____ Date _____

26. Port of call _____

_____

27. Purser _____

_____

28. Repositioning cruise _____

_____

29. Roll _____

_____

30. Schooner _____

_____

31. Single supplement _____

_____

32. Space ratio _____

_____

33. Stabilizer _____

_____

34. Stern _____

_____

35. Tender _____

_____

36. Third/fourth person rate _____

_____

37. Value season _____

_____

38. Windjammer _____

_____

(continued)

39. Yacht _____

_____

Name   Date

Directions: Go to page 249 to see an itinerary for Holland America's "Grand World Voyage," a 99-day voyage on the *Amsterdam.* Use the atlas in the back of the textbook to locate the stops on the cruise.

1. Choose one of the ports of call on the *Amsterdam*'s cruise, and research that port's main features and attractions. Construct a shore excursion of one day's duration that would take in those features and attractions. Use any travel resources available.

_____

_____

_____

_____

_____

_____

_____

_____

_____

_____

_____

_____

_____

_____

_____

_____

_____

_____

_____

_____

_____

(continued)

Directions: Mark the month or months during which cruises are popular in the following cruising areas.

Destination	February	July
2. Bermuda		
3. Hawaii		
4. Caribbean		
5. The Mediterranean		
6. Scandinavian fjords		
7. Alaska		

Name   Date

Directions: Suppose you have clients who are interested in booking a 5-day Caribbean cruise on Carnival's *Sensation*. Use the information on pages 250–256 (from Carnival's brochure and the *CLIA Manual*) to answer the following.

1. Your clients want to travel in June 2003. What options do they have for sailing dates?

   _____

2. Which deck has the most expensive accommodations?

   _____

3. Clients have asked you if they will have a chance to do any sightseeing while they are in Tampa. How would you respond?

   _____

   _____

4. How much are additional taxes per guest?

   _____

5. What guidelines does Carnival recommend for tipping

   a. the room steward?   _____

   b. the dining staff?   _____

   c. the maitre d'?   _____

6. What advice would you give clients who ask what clothes to bring?

   _____

   _____

7. When was the *Sensation* built?

   _____

8. How many dinner seatings are there each evening?

   _____

9. What is the normal cruise capacity?

   _____

10. How would you respond to clients who want to know what health or workout facilities are offered on the ship?

   _____

Name _____   Date _____

Directions: Use the information on Carnival's *Sensation* on pages 250–256 and Norwegian Cruise Lines' *Norway* on pages 257–260 to make the following comparisons.

	Norway	*Sensation* (5-day itinerary)
1. Departure point	_____	_____
2. Days at sea	_____	_____
3. Ports visited	_____	_____
4. Number of decks	_____	_____
5. Brochure rate for third and fourth persons (over the age of 14) in cabin	_____	_____
6. Per-person brochure rate of the most expensive cabin	_____	_____
7. Per-person brochure rate of the least expensive cabin	_____	_____
8. Deck location of casino	_____	_____
9. Number of swimming pools	_____	_____
10. Number of crew	_____	_____

Name   Date

Directions: Indicate whether the following statements are true or false. If part or all of the statement is false, explain why.

1. Cruising is mostly for senior citizens. True or false?

   _____

2. The longer the cruise, the older the passengers tend to be. True or false?

   _____

3. Cruises are popular, but they cost substantially more than land vacations. True or false?

   _____

4. Many cruises tend to be informal, with just one or two dress-up nights a week. True or false?

   _____

5. Cruises are a good way to see an island or an area in depth and to get to know its culture. True or false?

   _____

Directions: Answer the following questions.

6. Circle all of the following features that are *not* included in the basic price of *most* major cruises.

   (a) Meals   (b) Tips   (c) Port taxes   (d) Nightclub entertainment   (e) Sightseeing

   (f) Liquor   (g) Soft drinks   (h) Room (cabin) service   (i) Movies   (j) Transfers

7. What are four benefits of cruising?

   a. _____

   b. _____

   c. _____

   d. _____

8. What are two possible disadvantages of cruising?

   a. _____

   b. _____

(continued)

9. What are four factors that determine the price of a cruise?

   a. _____

   b. _____

   c. _____

   d. _____

10. Why might a client prefer an inside cabin?

    _____

    _____

11. What are three great rivers that lend themselves to cruising?

    _____

12. To what types of travelers might you suggest the first sitting?

    _____

Name   Date

Directions: Find CLIA's Web site, and then complete the following exercises.

1. Enter your zip code at the "Cruise Expert Locator" section of CLIA's Web site. Write the names of the travel agencies in your area that are CLIA affiliates.

   _____

   _____

2. CLIA's "Special Interest Guides" lists two types of activities to entice golf-lovers to take a cruise. What are they?

   _____

   _____

3. Choose five activities from the features listed under the "Special Interest Guides" that you think might be most important for a family cruising with two teenagers.

   a. _____

   b. _____

   c. _____

   d. _____

   e. _____

4. Find the list of North American Ports of Embarkation Links on CLIA's Web site. How many North American ports of embarkation are listed?

   _____

Directions: To gain practice in exploring other Web sites that help you learn about and sell cruises, complete the following exercises.

5. Go to the Web site of *Porthole* magazine. Choose one of the news articles in the "Cruise News" section, and list its topic.

   _____

6. Find the Web site of the International Council of Cruise Lines. Choose one interesting fact about cruising in the site's "Cruise Industry FAQs." Write the fact here, and be prepared to relate it to your fellow students.

   _____

(continued)

7. Two 20-year-olds are planning a cruise on Holland America for their honeymoon. What should a travel counselor be sure they know before booking them? See "Planning & Advice" under the tab that reads "For Booked Guests." On that screen, click on "Children and youth" under the "Traveling with Holland America" headline. On the next screen, click on "Guests under 21."

_____

_____

_____

8. Is it possible for clients to book their shore excursions before departure on Royal Caribbean Cruise Line? What stipulations must they follow? See www.royalcaribbean.com. Click on "Before You Board," and then click on "Shore & Land Excursions."

_____

_____

_____

Name   Date

Directions: Consider the following concepts and issues. Conduct research to help you respond, and be prepared to discuss the topic in class. (Tip: Refer to the Web sites listed in the "Resources: On Cruises" section on page 204 of Chapter 7 of the *Travel Career Development* textbook and other resources.)

From Dying to Thriving

Passenger ocean liner travel was a dying industry once jet service across the Atlantic became affordable and accessible to many. Establishing year-round cruising and highlighting the "pampering" experience of the ship while you sample exotic destinations was a brilliant move that launched today's cruise industry. This once-dying industry is now thriving.

Write two to four paragraphs that include:

- why you think this sector of the travel industry is doing so well.
- what percentage of the market it has gained (in other words, the number of people who have cruised).
- what the potential is for growth of the industry.
- what are some of the newest features and services being introduced and offered by the cruise industry (after doing some research).
- what your predictions are for the future of the cruise industry.

Name _____ Date _____

Directions: Define the following terms.

1. Adventure tour _____

   _____

2. Affinity group _____

   _____

3. Cancellation penalty _____

   _____

4. Ecotour _____

   _____

5. Escorted tour _____

   _____

6. FIT _____

   _____

7. Fly/drive _____

   _____

8. Hard adventure _____

   _____

9. Host _____

   _____

10. Hosted tour _____

   _____

11. Independent tour _____

   _____

12. Land rate _____

   _____

(continued)

13. NTA _____

_____

14. Package _____

_____

15. Shell _____

_____

16. Soft adventure _____

_____

17. Special-interest tour _____

_____

18. Step-on guide _____

_____

19. Template _____

_____

20. Tour _____

_____

21. Tour escort _____

_____

22. Tour guide _____

_____

23. Tour operator _____

_____

24. Tour wholesaler _____

_____

25. USTOA _____

_____

Name

Date

Directions: Indicate which type of tour is described by each of the following statements.

Description	Type of Tour
1. Also known as an FIT	a. Independent tour
2. Although all tours are sometimes called "packages," this type is most often called by that name.	b. Hosted tour
3. Involves traveling with a group, limiting freedom of choice and action	c. Escorted tour
4. A fly-drive, for example	d. Customized tour
5. Most often chosen for a trip to Las Vegas	
6. Very often chosen for a trip to a Caribbean island	
7. Most likely choice for Americans traveling to China	
8. An African safari, a specialized version of this type of tour	

(continued)

Directions: For those destinations you are familiar with, indicate which special interest it might be associated with; then research the other destinations and indicate which special interests they might be associated with. Add the state or country in which the destination is located.

Special interest

a. Skiing   b. Diving   c. Tennis   d. Art   e. Music

f. Theater   g. Ancient history   h. Mountain climbing   i. Wildlife viewing   j. Religion

Destination

9. Sun Valley

10. Hilton Head

11. Santa Fe

12. Branson

13. Marathon Key

14. Athens

15. Lourdes

16. Masai Mara

17. London

18. The Matterhorn

Name _____   Date _____

Directions: Answer the following questions on Cosmos Tour's "Alpine Adventure" by consulting pages 261–263.

1. How many days will clients travel, including the flight from the United States?

   _____

2. How many days will clients travel in Europe?

   _____

3. How many nights will clients spend in Europe?

   _____

4. How many countries are visited on this tour, and what are they?

   _____

5. In which cities does the group spend more than one night?

   _____

6. What hotel is used in or near Frankfurt?

   _____

7. What is the total price (including land and air) per person, double occupancy, for the July 7 departure of tour 6060?

   _____

8. What is the land-only price per person, double occupancy, for the October 6 departure of tour 6060?

   _____

9. Your clients are particularly interested in taking a cable car to the top of a mountain in Switzerland for a great view of the Alps. Where will they have the opportunity to do so? Is the cable car trip included in the cost of the tour?

   _____

10. Your clients are trying to plan how much money to take for extras. How would you summarize what is not included in their tour?

   _____

   _____

   _____

(continued)

11. Is there a supplement for single passengers for tour 6060? If so, what is it?

    _____

12. What deposit must a couple pay to book a tour?

    _____

13. How many days before departure must final payment be made for this tour?

    _____

14. If clients book a tour 30 days in advance, when must they make final payment?

    _____

15. If two clients cancel a $1,000-per-person tour 30 days in advance, what refund will they receive?

    _____

16. Can a traveler take two large suitcases on this tour? Explain.

    _____

17. Do these tours include à la carte meals or table d'hôte meals?

    _____

18. Can a person be thrown off the tour? Explain.

    _____

    _____

Name   Date

Directions: Provide the information requested.

1. Identify three features of tours that may benefit clients.

   a. _____

   b. _____

   c. _____

2. Identify three features of escorted tours, in particular, that may benefit clients.

   a. _____

   b. _____

   c. _____

3. Identify two drawbacks of escorted tours.

   a. _____

   b. _____

4. Describe three benefits that travel agencies derive from selling tours.

   a. _____

   b. _____

   c. _____

Directions: Circle the letter indicating the best answer.

5. What is most true about incentive tours?
   a. They are a good place to start for a travel counselor or associate of a tour company.
   b. Because they are free to the winners, accommodations and service need not be of the highest quality.
   c. They are generally combined with conventions and meetings.
   d. They should be meticulously planned and offer some special amenity or event.

6. The vast majority of tour prices listed in brochures are given
   a. per couple.
   b. per person double occupancy.
   c. per single person.
   d. per room.

(continued)

7. Full payment for tours is generally due
   a. 1 to 7 days before departure.
   b. 7 to 14 days before departure.
   c. 14 to 30 days before departure.
   d. 30 to 60 days before departure.

8. One good way of evaluating tour operators is to see if they are members of
   a. ASTA.
   b. WATA.
   c. USTOA.
   d. SITE.

Directions: Indicate whether following statements are true or false. If part or all of the statement is false, explain why.

9. The hallmark of a good escorted tour is that it changes hotels almost every night, enabling travelers to experience different things everyday. True or false?

   _____

   _____

10. A tour escort needs to be an expert in the area in which the tour is operating. True or false?

   _____

   _____

11. Those selling special-interest tours should become knowledgeable in that specialty before they start selling. True or false?

   _____

   _____

Name   Date

Directions: Search the Web to complete the following exercises.

1. What is the motto of the United States Tour Operators Association?

   _____

2. Choose a state in the United States that is in USTOA's list of destinations. What USTOA operators have tours to that state?

   _____

3. Look at "Join NTA" on the Web site of the National Tour Association, and then list the six categories of members that are part of this organization.

   _____

   _____

   _____

4. Answer the following questions about African Travel Inc.

   a. What is the average group size of their tours?

   _____

   b. What is the minimum group size?

   _____

   c. What association(s) is African Travel Inc. a member of?

   _____

5. Find information about Gray Line's "Best of Sydney" Tour. (If the tour is no longer listed at Gray Line's Web site, select another basic tour of a large city of your choice.)

   a. How long is the tour?

   _____

   b. How much does it cost in Australian dollars? (How much is that in U.S. dollars?)

   _____

6. Write the title of the lead article in this month's *Jax Fax Travel Marketing Magazine*. (Browse any of the other sections of its Web site that seem interesting.)

   _____

(continued)

7. After examining the Web site of *Specialty Travel Index*, choose a specialty area of travel that you might enjoy selling now or in the future. What tour operators offer this specialty? Choose an operator that sounds most interesting to you, visit its Web site, and jot down information that increases your passion for this specialty.

Specialty:

_____

Tour operators:

_____

_____

Selected operator:

_____

_____

_____

_____

_____

_____

Name   Date

Directions: Consider the following concepts and issues. Conduct research to help you respond, and be prepared to discuss the topic in class. (Tip: Refer to the Web sites listed in the "Resources: On Tours and Tour Operators" section on page 225 of Chapter 8 of the *Travel Career Development* textbook and other resources.)

Dynamic Packaging

According to the United States Tour Operator's Association (USTOA), today's travelers want to experience destinations more in-depth, including the local culture. However, Americans tend to take shorter trips than their European counterparts. Therefore, customized tours designed to match their interests and needs is very appealing to today's traveler. Tour operators and travel counselors are faced with the challenge of designing these tours to meet the needs of their customers and still make a profit. Some industry experts have proposed that technology can assist travel professionals with this challenge. "Dynamic Package" is using technology to assemble individual tour components and add a markup of the user's choosing, creating a custom-designed package with a single price in a matter of seconds.

Check several trade Web sites to learn the latest about dynamic packaging (pricing). Write two paragraphs regarding:
- What you learned about dynamic packaging
- How the industry views dynamic packaging
- What advantages and disadvantages you discovered
- Whether you think more industry professionals will use this new technology along with your reasons

Name　　　　　　　　　　　　　　　　　　　　　　Date

Directions: Define the following terms.

1. Bait-and-switch _____

_____

2. Cooperative advertising _____

_____

3. CRM _____

_____

4. Customer relationship marketing _____

_____

5. Direct mail _____

_____

6. Dual distribution _____

_____

7. Four Ps _____

_____

8. Marketing plan _____

_____

9. Market research _____

_____

10. Niche _____

_____

11. Promotion _____

_____

12. Public relations _____

_____

(continued)

13. Segmental analysis _____

_____

Name _____ Date _____

Directions: Choose the brand that you know the most about from the segments of the travel industry listed below. Explain how that brand markets itself in relation to each of the 4 Ps. In other words, describe its product, promotion techniques, the place where it makes its sales, and pricing strategy. (If you need to find more about the brand you chose, use resources such as the Internet.)

1. Hotels: Motel 6, Holiday Inn Express, Embassy Suites, or Ritz Carlton

    Brand selected _____

    a. Product _____

    b. Promotion _____

    c. Place _____

    d. Price _____

    e. Do any of these marketing decisions seem inconsistent? _____

2. Cruise lines: Carnival, Delta Queen, Windjammer, or Silversea

    Brand selected _____

    a. Product _____

    b. Promotion _____

    c. Place _____

    d. Price _____

    e. Do any of these marketing decisions seem inconsistent? _____

3. Car rental: Hertz, Alamo, or Enterprise

    Brand selected _____

    a. Product _____

    b. Promotion _____

    c. Place _____

    d. Price _____

    e. Do any of these marketing decisions seem inconsistent? _____

(continued)

Directions: Within each set of parentheses in the following sentence, circle one of the choices.

Your tour company runs *(deluxe, moderate-first class, budget)* *(adventure trips, religious pilgrimages, escorted sightseeing tours)* to *(Asia, Africa, South America)*.

(For instance, if you picked the first choice in each series, your sentence would read "Your tour company runs *deluxe adventure trips* to *Asia*.") Now, using specific examples, explain how a shift in each of the following might change your marketing strategy for selling these tours.

4. Demographics _____

   _____

   _____

5. Laws _____

   _____

   _____

6. Political situation _____

   _____

   _____

7. Economics _____

   _____

   _____

Name   Date

Directions: The agency you are affiliated with has blocked off 20 cabins on Carnival's *Sensation* for a 5-day Caribbean cruise. Staff members have had trouble finding customers and have only 30 days left to sell. They have asked for your advice in deciding how to promote the cruise. To answer the following questions, refer to the excerpts from the Carnival brochure on pages 250–255 and from the *CLIA Manual* on page 256.

1. What age group would you target? Why?

   _____

2. What income group would you target? Why?

   _____

3. Choose three of the following promotional methods, and briefly describe how you could use each to promote the cruise: (a) direct mail, (b) print advertising, (c) radio and television advertising, (d) the Internet, (e) Yellow Pages, (f) public relations, or (g) personal selling.

   a. _____

   _____

   b. _____

   _____

   c. _____

   _____

Directions: Using the list of promotional methods in question 3, indicate which method or methods you would use in each of the following situations. (Be prepared to explain why you chose it.)

4. A travel agency in northern Minneapolis wants to sell a broad range of products to the people on its side of the city.

   _____

5. A cruise line specializing in Alaskan cruises wants to be seen by the general public as being very concerned about its effect on the environment.

   _____

6. An incoming tour operator in New Orleans hopes to attract clients or groups all over the world to its "Authentic America" tours.

   _____

(continued)

7. A hotel finds that the next three weekends are very slow and wants to fill its rooms.

   _____

8. A new car rental chain wants to establish a foothold with companies in its region and is willing to offer them special incentives if their employees book its cars.

   _____

9. A travel agency wishes to sell a group tour to large church groups in its area.

   _____

10. An airline wants to announce its latest discount airfare, which will be available for the next two weeks.

    _____

11. A tour company wants to keep in touch with all travel counselors and clients who booked its tours in the past year.

    _____

12. Amtrak hopes to bolster its image so Congress will increase its funding for the next five years.

    _____

Name _____   Date _____

Directions: Answer the following questions.

1. What are five elements of the marketing process?

   a. _____

   b. _____

   c. _____

   d. _____

   e. _____

2. What type of information about a travel agency should be included in its Yellow Pages advertisement?

   _____

   _____

3. How does marketing differ from selling?

   _____

   _____

4. What are some reasons for a supplier to use dual distribution of its products?

   _____

   _____

5. How could a computerized database be helpful in the marketing process?

   _____

   _____

6. What is the difference between a product-oriented marketing strategy and a market-oriented strategy? Give an example of each.

   _____

   _____

(continued)

Directions: Indicate whether each of the following would produce an example of (a) primary data or (b) secondary data.

7. Talking to your clients after they return from a trip

   _____

8. Having your clients fill out a questionnaire after they return from a trip

   _____

9. Getting data from the TIA (Travel Industry of America) Web site

   _____

10. Doing telephone interviews with potential clients in your zip code

    _____

11. Studying a tour operator's report on the demographics of past clients

    _____

Worksheet 9.5 Technology Technique

Name   Date

Directions: Go to the Web sites www.abercrombiekent.com and www.gwvtravel.com (or others suggested by your instructor). Analyze how each deals with the four Ps discussed in Chapter 9.

Web site a. _____

Web site b. _____

1. Product

   a. _____

   _____

   b. _____

   _____

2. Promotion

   a. _____

   _____

   b. _____

   _____

3. Place

   a. _____

   _____

   b. _____

   _____

4. Price

   a. _____

   _____

   b. _____

   _____

Name   Date

Directions: Consider the following concepts and issues. Conduct research to help you respond, and be prepared to discuss the topic in class. (Tip: Refer to the Web sites listed in the "Resources: On Marketing" section on page 252 of Chapter 9 of the *Travel Career Development* textbook and other resources.)

Integrated Marketing

Marketing is no longer just for the "marketing department." Organizations of all sizes have realized that to compete in today's business world customer-focused marketing must be integrated into all their business processes from accounting to front-line interactions with the customers. Technology has provided tools (databases) that help professionals deliver personalized service.

In one to two paragraphs explain how front-line, entry-level travel professionals use the marketing concepts you learned in Chapter 9 in their everyday interactions with their customers.

_____

_____

_____

_____

_____

_____

_____

_____

_____

_____

_____

_____

_____

_____

_____

_____

_____

_____

_____

_____

Name _____　　　　Date _____

Directions: Define the following terms.

1. Body language _____

_____

2. Close-ended question _____

_____

3. Cross-selling _____

_____

4. Feedback question _____

_____

5. Open-ended question _____

_____

6. Outside sales agent _____

_____

7. Selling up _____

_____

Name   Date

Directions: *Travel Career Development* breaks the sales process into eight basic steps. Number the following questions and statements in the order that they would most likely occur during the sales process. Please note that one of the sales steps is represented by two statements.

_____ So, should we book the Club Med or the Sandals resort for you?

_____ Did you have any specific place in mind for this winter's trip?

_____ Your documents should be in any day, and I will call you and deliver them as soon as they arrive.

_____ I've found two tours of Eastern Europe that would best match the general list of places you want to visit. Let me point out the highlights of each of them on this large map of the area.

_____ The *Sensation* offers both of the sports that you enjoy, and it visits the ports that you are most interested in.

_____ Ah, an excellent choice of hotel! Will that be check or credit card?

_____ Ah, a beautiful spot for scuba-diving; I snorkeled there once myself.

_____ Yes, it does tend to rain a lot, but that's what makes Ireland so lush and green all year.

_____ I see; so tickets to the Vienna Boys' Choir, the Spanish Riding School, and the Salzburg festival are absolutely essential for your trip to Austria this summer.

Name   Date

Directions: Describe a benefit that each of the following features might offer a client.

1. We can reserve and ticket any airline.

   _____

   _____

2. All our counselors have traveled extensively.

   _____

   _____

3. We deliver tickets.

   _____

   _____

4. The price of this tour is all-inclusive.

   _____

   _____

5. This tour has a step-on guide at each stop.

   _____

   _____

6. This tour includes round-trip transfers.

   _____

   _____

7. Your hotel is right on the beach.

   _____

   _____

8. Your hotel is in a remote location.

   _____

   _____

(continued)

9. All meals are included.

_____

_____

10. No meals are included.

_____

_____

Worksheet 10.4 Gathering Information, Making Recommendations, and Closing

Name _____   Date _____

Directions: Your clients, Mr. and Mrs. Safire, and their two children, ages 14 and 8, are planning a vacation to Disney World in Orlando, Florida. They are having a difficult time choosing a hotel. Write five questions that will enable you to discover their expectations and needs so that you can recommend a hotel. Label each question as open-ended, close-ended, or feedback. Make sure that you include at least one question from each category.

1. _____

   _____

2. _____

   _____

3. _____

   _____

4. _____

   _____

5. _____

   _____

Directions: Indicate whether each of the following recommendations is appropriate (A) or inappropriate (I). If it is inappropriate, rephrase it to make it appropriate.

6. I know you're going to love Disney World because all my clients do. A or I?

   _____

7. As you can see on the map, your hotel is right on the beach. A or I?

   _____

8. You have to eat at Babbo. It's the best restaurant in New York. A or I?

   _____

9. This tour meets all the requirements that you outlined. A or I?

   _____

10. The weather is always perfect in St. Thomas. A or I?

   _____

(continued)

Directions: The following attempts at closing a sale are so poor that they are more likely to lose the sale than to close it. Describe what is wrong with each and how you would change it.

11. Would you like to make a reservation today, or would you like to go home and think about it?

_____

_____

_____

_____

_____

12. Which of the seven brochures have you decided has the best package for you?

_____

_____

_____

_____

_____

13. That resort usually has rooms available at this time of year up to the last minute, so call me any time.

_____

_____

_____

_____

_____

14. Are you sure you want to book Tahiti? Fiji looks just as good, and Hawaii is even less expensive.

_____

_____

_____

_____

_____

Name   Date

Directions: Indicate whether the following statements are true or false. If part or all of the statement is false, explain why.

1. When a traveler has bought a vacation and has plane tickets and hotel vouchers in hand, he or she has purchased a tangible product. True or false?

_____

2. Leisure travel, by its very nature, is discretionary. True or false?

_____

3. A client who leans towards you with an open hand is exhibiting body language that indicates a readiness to buy. True or false?

_____

4. When people cross their arms or legs, they are exhibiting body language that indicates that they accept what you are saying. True or false?

_____

5. Benefits are more important than features. True or false?

_____

Directions: Each of the following questions illustrates two types or categories of question. For each question, indicate the two types it illustrates, using the choices below. For example, "You wouldn't be thinking of buying this trip now, would you?" is an example of both a closing question and a close-ended question (but a very poor one).

Type

a. Qualifying   b. Open-ended   c. Close-ended   d. Closing   e. Feedback

Question

6. How many people will be in your party?   _____   _____

7. Would you like to take the cruise on the 21st or the 28th?   _____   _____

8. What would your dream trip look like if you could plan it any way you want?   _____   _____

9. Are you saying you want to see all five countries in the Alps on this trip?   _____   _____

10. What kinds of hotels do you usually stay in?   _____   _____

(continued)

Directions: Provide the information requested.

11. List five qualifying questions that are appropriate to ask if you are selling travel.

    a. _____

    b. _____

    c. _____

    d. _____

    e. _____

12. Describe two tools that you could use when presenting recommendations to clients.

    a. _____

    b. _____

13. Give two examples of how you could cross-sell to a client who called only to rent a car.

    a. _____

    b. _____

14. Describe how travel counselors can ensure customer satisfaction after a sale is made.

    _____

    _____

    _____

Name   Date

Directions: Table 10.1 on pages 258–259 in *Travel Career Development* lists motives for leisure travel and destinations that might appeal to travelers with those motives. Using the Web as a source for destinations, name one destination not listed in Table 10.1 that is likely to appeal to travelers with the following motives.

1. Gambling _____

2. Shopping _____

3. Religion _____

4. Sun _____

5. Food and drink _____

6. Entertainment _____

7. Arts _____

8. History and culture _____

9. Personal challenge _____

10. Ecotourism _____

11. Sightseeing _____

12. Relaxation _____

13. Active sports _____

Directions: For practice using the Web to expand your knowledge about selling techniques, complete the following exercises.

14. Go to CLIA's Web site, click on "Travel Agents," and search the categories listed. Choose the sales seminar that you might consider taking first when you are in the industry.

_____

15. Enter the word "selling" in the Search box at *Travel Weekly*'s Web site, www.travelweekly.com. How many articles are listed that deal with the topic in some way?

_____

16. Search for an article on sales tips or techniques by entering terms such as "selling techniques," "sales tips," and "sales seminars" in the Search box at *Travel Weekly*'s Web site. Describe an idea about selling that is not included in your textbook.

_____

Name   Date

Directions: Consider the following concepts and issues. Conduct research to help you respond, and be prepared to discuss the topic in class. (Tip: Refer to the Web sites listed in the "Resources: On Selling" section on page 277 of Chapter 10 of the *Travel Career Development* textbook and other resources.)

Is It Service or Sales?

Salespeople are not selling products—they are fulfilling the needs of their customers. They can't fulfill those needs if they haven't discovered them. In the process of uncovering client's needs and matching products and services to meet those needs, sales professionals build relationships with their customers. Clients feel served or serviced rather than sold. This distinction is critical to the long-term success of any sales professional. In your own words, write one to two paragraphs about how customer-focused sales (uncovering needs and building relationships) benefit (1) the seller, (2) the customer, and (3) the company or business.

_____

_____

_____

_____

_____

_____

_____

_____

_____

_____

_____

_____

_____

_____

_____

_____

_____

_____

_____

_____

_____

Name _____   Date _____

Directions: Define the following terms.

1. Baggage and personal possessions insurance _____

   _____

2. CEIR _____

   _____

3. CIC _____

   _____

4. Commercial agency _____

   _____

5. Flight insurance _____

   _____

6. Incentive house _____

   _____

7. Meeting _____

   _____

8. Meeting planner _____

   _____

9. MPI _____

   _____

10. SATH _____

    _____

11. SITE _____

    _____

12. Travel accident and health insurance _____

    _____

(continued)

13. Travelers with disabilities _____

_____

14. Trip cancellation or interruption insurance _____

_____

Worksheet 11.2 Travelers with Disabilities

Name   Date

Directions: Indicate whether each statement is true or false. If a statement is false, explain why.

1. A bulkhead seat generally is a good choice for a physically disabled person because of the extra legroom. True or false?

2. A seat in the emergency exit row is generally a good choice for a physically disabled person because of the extra legroom. True or false?

3. Blind people are allowed to take their Seeing Eye dogs on flights. True or false?

4. All Amtrak coaches are equipped to transport passengers with disabilities. True or false?

5. Most long-distance motorcoach services in the United States have wheelchair lifts on the coach. True or false?

6. Most car rental companies can provide hand-controlled vehicles for renters with disabilities. True or false?

7. At least one bathroom aboard most of today's planes can accommodate passengers in wheelchairs. True or false?

8. Most cruise ships carry Seeing Eye dogs aboard at no extra cost. True or false?

9. Special provisions must be made to take a battery-operated wheelchair on a flight. True or false?

10. Passengers with disabilities can order food and drink at their seats on Amtrak. True or false?

Name

Date

Directions: Answer the following questions.

1. Mr. Fastow is afraid that if he becomes ill or has an accident before his trip, he may lose all or most of the money that he pays for the trip. How can you help him?

_____

_____

_____

2. Mr. Skilling's mother is ill. He is afraid that if she takes a turn for the worse, he will have to cancel his trip and will lose all or most of the money he pays for the trip. Can you help him and, if so, how?

_____

_____

_____

3. Ms. Watkins usually travels with very expensive clothing for presentations and award ceremonies. She is afraid that if the airline loses her luggage, her loss will far exceed the compensation from the airline. Can you lessen her fears?

_____

_____

_____

4. The Lands are 72-year-olds and will be traveling overseas for the first time since they retired. They are concerned that Medicare doesn't cover them in other countries. Are their concerns valid, and can you ease them?

_____

_____

_____

5. Shelly Mattura is a single mom who is starting her own business and flying a lot to meet people. She is concerned about flying and worried that if anything happens to her, her daughter will be left without enough funds for school. Can you ease her concerns?

_____

_____

_____

(continued)

6. A group of trekkers are going to explore the source of the Zambezi River in Africa. They wonder what might happen to them in case of illness or accident while they are in the bush away from civilization. What can you do for them?

_____

_____

_____

7. Three years ago, when your client lived in another city, he booked a cruise with a line that went bankrupt before the date of the cruise. It took him two years to get some of his money back, and he didn't get much. He doesn't want to take the chance that this could happen again. How can you reassure him?

_____

_____

_____

Name _____   Date _____

Directions: Provide the following information.

1. Name two characteristics of business travel that make it an advantageous market for travel agencies.

   a. _____

   b. _____

2. List several key needs specific to business travelers.

   _____

   _____

   _____

   _____

3. Choose two of the following types of specialized groups, and briefly describe the special service they require: senior citizens, honeymooners, members of a religious group, or family travelers.

   a. _____

   _____

   b. _____

   _____

4. Name three things that a meeting planner might do that most travel counselors would not see as their function.

   a. _____

   b. _____

   c. _____

5. Comment on the following statement: "Because incentive trips are usually given free as rewards, they do not have to meet the high standards of trips that travelers pay for themselves."

   _____

   _____

   _____

   _____

(continued)

Directions: Heather Hardaway decided to sell group travel, but her first attempts were not very successful. Below are some the steps she took. What changes would you recommend in each step?

6. Because she loves skiing, Heather decided to sell ski trips to organizations in her area.

   _____

   _____

   _____

7. She contacted the president of one social club and gave a presentation to her.

   _____

   _____

   _____

8. She met with another organization at its monthly meeting and provided members with many destination choices, from Utah to Vermont. She even mentioned the most famous places in the Alps. She also made it clear that she was happy to book any week they chose.

   _____

   _____

   _____

9. When Heather finally sold a trip to one small group, she booked all of the arrangements directly with hotels, transportation companies, and ski facilities. Participants later said they were dissatisfied with the location of the hotels relative to the ski lifts and with the fact that the transportation did not run to the resort when their plane was late.

   _____

   _____

   _____

10. For the group that she booked, Heather made sure she received a 10 percent commission on all her arrangements. She figured that because she earns a 10 percent commission when she arranges travel for two people, making the same arrangements for 20 to 30 people at one time at that rate would give her a hefty profit.

   _____

   _____

   _____

Name   Date

Directions: Use the Web to answer the following questions.

1. In what specialty areas does ASTA offer home-study courses?

   _____

   _____

   _____

2. What ship that services the North American market has the most wheelchair-accessible cabins? What else does this ship offer passengers with a physical disability? (Tip: Refer to the Web sites listed in the "Resources: On Specialized Sales" section on page 300 of Chapter 11 of the *Travel Career Development* textbook and other resources.)

   _____

   _____

   _____

3. Where will the next World Congress of the Society for Accessible Travel and Hospitality be held?

   _____

4. What specialty trip described at the Web site of the *Specialty Travel Index* would you like to take and love to sell to others?

   _____

5. Go to some of the Web sites related to meetings and conventions that are listed in the "Resources: On Specialized Sales" section on page 300 of the textbook. Describe an insight or interesting fact that you learned from one of these Web sites, and be prepared to share it with your fellow students.

   _____

   _____

   _____

Name   Date

Directions: Consider the following concepts and issues. Conduct research to help you respond, and be prepared to discuss the topic in class. (Tip: Refer to the Web sites listed in the "Resources: On Specialized Sales" section on page 300 of Chapter 11 of the *Travel Career Development* textbook and other resources.)

Developing a Niche

Specializing in a specific area or niche has been the formula for success for many travel professionals. The niche they choose can be a type of travel, a specific segment of the market (type of traveler), or a destination. Whichever they choose, they create a distinctive identity and establish themselves as experts in meeting the special needs of this niche.

Explore the leading travel organization's Web sites to learn more about developing a niche in the travel industry. Answer the following questions in one paragraph each:

- What factors should I consider when choosing a niche or specialization?
- What resources are available to help me develop my expertise in a niche?

Name _____　　Date _____

Directions: Define the following terms.

1. E-mail _____

_____

2. Fax _____

_____

3. Videoconferencing _____

_____

4. Voice mail _____

_____

5. Webcasting _____

_____

Worksheet 12.2 Selling by Telephone

Name   Date

Directions: Answer the following questions.

1. What are three steps you can take to compensate for the ways that the telephone distorts the human voice?

   a. _____

   b. _____

   c. _____

2. What are three techniques that you can use when selling by telephone in order to help make up for the absence of body language?

   a. _____

   b. _____

   c. _____

Directions: Translate the following statements into language that a novice traveler can understand easily.

3. (By a travel counselor) My CRT shows that flight is a no-op on 7-12.

   _____

   _____

4. (By a member of the cruise staff) You'll have to tender in at that port.

   _____

   _____

Directions: In the following scenarios, a potential client calls a travel agency and a travel counselor responds. How would you improve the travel counselor's response to these callers in order to convert them to buyers?

5. "I saw an ad in the Sunday paper from ABC Travel for a $199 airfare from Los Angeles to Boston. Can you book it?"

   "I've never heard of that fare."

   _____

   _____

   _____

(continued)

6. "I just read an interesting article about Bermuda. I'll probably never go, but I'd like to know more. Do you have any information you could send me?"

   "Call the Bermuda Department of Tourism for general information, and then call us back if you ever decide to go."

   _____

   _____

   _____

7. "What can you tell me about tours to Alaska?"

   "There's too much information to explain on the telephone. You'll have to come in to the office."

   _____

   _____

   _____

8. "I'd like to speak to someone in your office who has been on a safari."

   "No one here has ever been. Sorry."

   _____

   _____

   _____

Name   Date

Directions: Circle the correctly spelled word in each of the following word groups.

1. accomodation   accommodation

2. itinerery   itinerary

3. luxury   luxery

4. computer   computor

5. commission   commision

6. cancelation   cancellation

7. insurance   insurence

8. occupancy   occupency

9. guarantee   guarentee

10. delux   deluxe

Directions: Indicate which of the following words is spelled correctly, and write the correct spelling for the incorrect ones.

11. separate   _____

12. occured   _____

13. Carribean   _____

14. Britian   _____

15. inoculation   _____

16. overide   _____

17. benefited   _____

18. accompanied   _____

19. reccommend   _____

20. Mediterrainean   _____

Name   Date

Directions: Your agency has received the following letter:

> To Whom it May Concern:
>
> I am writing to express my concern about some things that happened to me on my recent trip to Denver, which I booked through your agency.
>
> I know I saved money by flying Air Apparent from here to Chicago and connecting with the big airline there, but I did not realize that I would have to carry my bags so much. They told me that I could not send my bags all the way through to Denver and as a result I had to carry them up two flights of stairs and a very long distance at the Chicago airport. This threw my back out and I had to spend the first two days at my sister-in-law's house lying on a couch. I distinctly remember that last year I was able to send my bags all the way through from here to Denver.
>
> When I came back from Denver, I missed my flight because the lady told me I had not arrived in time. That was a lie. I was at the airport waiting for an hour and then was in the bathroom when they told us to get on the plane so I did not hear the announcement. You told me that if I had my boarding ticket, which you gave me, I could get right on the plane, but the lady at the gate said that someone else had my seat!
>
> I had to wait for the next flight and my brother, who flies all the time, says I should have gotten at least $300 in compensation.
>
> I am very angry about this and feel that I should be compensated.
>
> Yours sincerely,

Write a reply to explain what happened. Consider the following:
- How could the baggage problem have occurred?
- How could the boarding confusion have occurred?
- What are the rules regarding denied boarding compensation?

_____

_____

_____

_____

_____

_____

_____

(continued)

Worksheet 12.5 Chapter Review

Name _____   Date _____

Directions: Answer the following questions.

1. When is a memo likely to be your best form of communication?

   _____

   _____

2. What are four elements that a procedure or policy manual should contain?

   a. _____

   b. _____

   c. _____

   d. _____

3. What are five guidelines for using e-mail effectively?

   a. _____

   b. _____

   c. _____

   d. _____

   e. _____

Directions: For each of the following situations, indicate which method of communication is likely to be most effective: (a) face-to-face, (b) written letter, (c) fax, (d) phone call, or (e) e-mail.

4. Your airline just received a letter of complaint from a traveler, and you need to clarify what happened before you can act.

   _____

5. Documents have been received at your travel agency, and you want to inform the client that they are being sent out today.

   _____

6. Your hotel has just received a request for 15 rooms a month from now from a small tour company. You want to inform the booking agent at the tour company about payment deadlines, cancellation penalties, and other stipulations concerning the reservation.

   _____

(continued)

7. A client whose business travel you have booked for the past three months wants to take a trip to Europe with her family next year and asks for information.

   _____

8. A client who took one of your tour packages contacted his travel counselor who, in turn, has contacted you and described in detail the promised amenities that he did not receive. They request a partial refund A.S.A.P.

   _____

9. Your boss has decided on a major new sales campaign and wants you to contact the high-volume travel agencies in your area to explain it to them.

   _____

10. You need to inform a colleague about a meeting scheduled next week, but you know he's out of the office today.

   _____

11. A client is going to Turkmenistan in two months, and you want to tell her about passport and visa regulations, State Department warnings and suggestions, and available insurance.

   _____

12. You want your client to go over the detailed itinerary that you have prepared for his four-week journey to China.

   _____

13. A client's reservation is about to be canceled because she has not paid her deposit.

   _____

Name   Date

Directions: For additional practice using the Web, complete the following exercises.

1. Look up the word *infrastructure* at www.dictionary.com, and list items in the definition that relate to tourism.

   _____

   _____

   _____

2. Go to www.email.about.com, and write one tip about e-mail that was not included in the textbook. Tip: It might be helpful to enter "writing email" (with no hyphen) into the Search box.

   _____

   _____

   _____

3. How much does it cost to send a one-ounce airmail letter to London via the U.S. mail? Go to the postal service at www.usps.com; click first on "Calculate Postage" and then on "Calculate International Postage."

   _____

Name   Date

Directions: Consider the following concepts and issues. Conduct research to help you respond, and be prepared to discuss the topic in class. (Tip: Refer to the Web sites listed in the "Resources: On Communications" section on page 318 of Chapter 12 of the *Travel Career Development* textbook and other resources.)

Webcasts

You are a corporate travel counselor who specializes in meeting planning. One of your clients has asked you to join a webcast meeting scheduled for next Tuesday with the managers of six branch offices to discuss the upcoming conference that you have been planning. Your client has set up a password for you to join this real-time private online meeting. Your computer has the necessary system requirements, software (media player for audio) and video camera (visual). Would you communicate differently during the webcast than you would in a face-to-face meeting? List any special considerations you would make to ensure that you communicate effectively during the webcast. (Hint: Include both audio and visual considerations).

Name _____ Date _____

Directions: Define the following terms.

1. Accountable document _____

_____

2. ARC report _____

_____

3. Area bank _____

_____

4. Area Bank Settlement Plan _____

_____

5. Base fare _____

_____

6. Cash flow _____

_____

7. Consortium _____

_____

8. Escrow account _____

_____

9. Income statement _____

_____

10. Invoice _____

_____

11. MCO _____

_____

12. PTA _____

_____

(continued)

13. Receipt _____

_____

14. Tour order _____

_____

15. Voucher _____

_____

_____

Name   Date

Directions: State whether each of the following is a (a) fixed expense, (b) variable expense, or (c) semivariable (mixed) expense.

1. Rent   _____

2. Advertising   _____

3. Commissions to outside salespersons
   and bonuses to employees   _____

4. Salaries   _____

5. Telephone service   _____

6. Insurance   _____

Directions: On a particular day you made the following bookings. Assume a 10 percent commission on all components unless stated otherwise; do not include port charges or any taxes in your calculations. What commission will you earn for each booking? (When necessary, refer to the brochure excerpts in Part 2 of this workbook for more information.)

7. Hyatt Regency Aruba Resort & Casino for two people in a double for two nights at a rate of $235 per night.

   _____

8. Hyatt Regency Aruba Resort & Casino for two people, each in a single room, for two nights, at a rate of $205 per night.

   _____

9. A Hertz car rental at the rate of $199 weekly and $39 per extra day. The car is picked up on June 1 at 9 A.M. and returned on June 11 at 5 P.M.

   _____

10. Cosmos Tour's "Alpine Adventure," for two people in one room, land and air, for departure on October 6. (See pages 261–263.)

   _____

11. A party of four adults whose airline tickets come to $3,200 (base fare) with a 7 percent commission rate and a $50 commission cap.

   _____

12. A party of four adults whose airline tickets come to $1,200 (base fare) with a 7 percent commission rate and a $50 commission cap.

   _____

(continued)

13. A client takes Amtrak from Washington to New York for $199 round trip. He rents a car for three days at $49 per day and stays at a hotel for three nights at $189 per night. What is the total commission you will earn for his trip?

_____

14. You have sold a deluxe tour to two clients for $6,000. A comprehensive insurance policy including trip cancellation/ interruption, medical/accident coverage, and baggage insurance will cost them $150 per person. The insurance company pays you 30 percent commission. What will your commission be on the entire trip, including the insurance?

_____

15. The cruise you have sold costs $1,299 per person, double occupancy. Your two clients already have paid a $200-per-person deposit.

   a. When final payment is due, how much must you collect?

_____

   b. What is your total commission?

_____

   c. How much will you now send to the cruise line for final payment after deducting your commission?

_____

16. When you sell $20,000 worth of tours with A-B-C Tours, you receive a 2 percent override above your 10 percent commission.

   a. How much is the override?

_____

   b. The override represents what percent increase in your commission?

_____

Name   Date

Directions: Answer the following questions.

1. A travel agency is owed $650 in hotel commissions and $4,000 from a group for a deposit that you have forwarded to hold space on a cruise. Is the $4,650 listed on your balance sheet under assets or liabilities?

   _____

2. Is the amount of equity or the amount of stock held by the owners of a company listed on the balance sheet as an asset or a liability?

   _____

3. Is the financial position of a business at a particular time found on the income statement or the balance sheet?

   _____

4. Is a summary of revenue and expenses over three months done on the income statement or the balance sheet?

   _____

5. Besides wanting to avoid the need to pay immediately or to carry large amounts of cash, what is another major reason that clients may wish to pay by credit card in foreign countries?

   _____

Directions: Indicate whether each statement is true or false. If the statement is false, explain why.

6. You can accept a credit card from a stranger over the phone as long as you receive an approval code through your computer or via phone. True or false?

   _____

7. You can accept a personal check from a stranger as long as he or she shows you a picture ID and signs the check in front of you. True or false?

   _____

8. You can accept traveler's checks from a stranger as long as he or she shows you a passport or other ID that matches his or her name and signature. True or false?

   _____

9. You can accept cash from a stranger as long as it's not counterfeit. True or false?

   _____

10. Most agencies prefer to accept a credit card from a stranger rather than a check. True or false?

   _____

(continued)

Directions: Circle the letter indicating the best answer to each question.

11. Which of the following expenses makes up the largest part of a typical travel agency's budget?
    a. Rent
    b. Salaries
    c. Computer leases
    d. Taxes on corporate profits

12. Sales of this travel component still represent a huge part of a travel agency's income, although commission rates fell steadily from 1995 to 2001.
    a. Airlines
    b. Hotels
    c. Car rentals
    d. Tours

13. Commissions for this product are generally in the 20 to 35 percent range, reflecting the large amount of work required for a smaller gross sale than for most products.
    a. Tours
    b. Cruises
    c. Travel insurance
    d. Rail tickets

14. Commissions from these two travel components are usually received by agencies after the client's trip.
    a. Airlines and hotels
    b. Hotels and car rentals
    c. Car rentals and tours
    d. Airlines and car rentals

Name   Date

Directions: Answer the following questions.

1. Write one rule or reminder about in-office ticket security that you find at ARC's Web site.

   _____

   _____

   _____

   _____

2. Go to *Travel Weekly*'s Web site and enter "overrides" in its Search box. Choose one article to summarize in a sentence or two.

   _____

   _____

   _____

   _____

3. Go to the Web site of a travel agency consortium (you can try www.ensembledirect.com), and list the financial benefits that this organization offers to its members.

   _____

   _____

   _____

   _____

Name   Date

Directions: Consider the following concepts and issues. Conduct research to help you respond, and be prepared to discuss the topic in class.

Travel Agency Profitability

The methods in which travel agencies make money have shifted. Some agencies didn't adapt to the changes in the industry well and closed their doors. Others have found creative ways to provide new services to their clients and are adopting sound business practices that allow them to make healthy profits.

Explore the Web sites of two well-known consulting companies that have helped many travel agencies adjust their business models, and thrive in the new marketplace.
  1. Joselyn, Tepper, & Associates (JTA) www.joselyntepper.com
  2. Visionistics, www.visionistics.com

Based on the information found on these two Web sites, what actions and strategies can travel agencies take to become and remain profitable? Write two paragraphs that include some of these strategies along with an explanation as to why you believe these strategies can be successful.

Name _____   Date _____

Directions: Define the following terms.

1. Business plan _____

    _____

2. Errors and omissions and general liability insurance _____

    _____

3. Independent contractor _____

    _____

4. Independent contractor network _____

    _____

5. NACTA _____

    _____

6. OSSN _____

    _____

7. Telecommute _____

    _____

Name   Date

Directions: Indicate the resource that would provide you with the information described in each of the following statements.

Description of information   **Reference/Resource**

1. Maps and listings of discounted airfares
   and tours divided by regions of the world   _____   a. CLIA *Manual*

2. Detailed cruise line and ship information,   b. *Hotel & Travel Index*
   port descriptions, and sales policies   _____
                                                                         c. *Specialty Travel Index*
3. Airport maps and ground service information _____
                                                                         d. STAR Service
4. Suppliers that offer discounted domestic
   and international airfares   _____   e. JAX FAX

5. Travel writers' critiques of individual   f. *Moffit's Consolidator Guide*
   hotel properties   _____
                                                                         g. Travel Agent Directory
6. Hotel properties rated into 1 of 10
   categories   _____   h. OAG Business Travel

7. List of suppliers grouped into
   categories by products and services   _____

8. List of tours by activity and
   geographical location   _____

_____

Name   Date

Directions: Provide the information requested.

1. List three factors that have contributed to the increasing numbers of home-based travel agencies.

   a. _____

   _____

   b. _____

   _____

   c. _____

   _____

2. List the criteria that must be met for the IRS to consider a home-based agent an independent contractor.

   a. _____

   b. _____

   c. _____

   d. _____

   e. _____

   f. _____

3. A business plan includes the following three components:

   a. _____

   _____

   b. _____

   _____

   c. _____

   _____

(continued)

4. Describe one advantage and one disadvantage of creating a home-based office to sell travel.

    a. Advantage

    _____

    a. Disadvantage

    _____

5. Once an agency's Web site is up and running, what additional tasks need to be done on a regular basis?

    a. _____

    b. _____

    c. _____

Directions: Circle the letter indicating the best answer.

6. When selecting a host agency, independent contractors should consider
    a. if the host agency's specialization fits well with the independent contractor's niche.
    b. the agency's experience working with independent contractors.
    c. the level of support the independent contractor needs compared to the level of support the host agency will give.
    d. all of the above.

7. Home-based agents can develop their networks by
    a. establishing relationships with suppliers that specialize in the same niche.
    b. joining trade organizations.
    c. attending seminars, workshops, and trade shows.
    d. all of the above.

8. A pseudo identification number
    a. is recognized by a single supplier.
    b. is recognized by U.S. travel suppliers only.
    c. is recognized by the majority of travel suppliers worldwide.
    d. may be required by the state.

9. Customer relationship management is a business strategy that combines
    a. upgrades and selling-up.
    b. personalized service and technology
    c. cross-selling and technology.
    d. marketing and finance.

10. An employee of an agency who works out of his or her home is a(n)
    a. independent contractor.
    b. flex-employee.
    c. telecommuter.
    d. host agent.

Name   Date

Directions: Search the Web in order to complete the following exercises.

1. Browse the contents of the "Home-Based Travel Agent Resource Center" at www.homebasedtravelagent.com. Answer the following questions.

    a. What scams does the author warn the reader to be cautious about?

    _____

    b. Name three professional resources that are listed on this Web site.

    1. _____

    2. _____

    3. _____

2. Go to www.hometravelagency.com and find the article "Home-Based Agent Qualities That Lead to Success." List the qualities below.

    a. _____

    b. _____

    c. _____

    d. _____

    e. _____

    f. _____

3. List three benefits of joining NACTA.

    a. _____

    b. _____

    c. _____

4. How many members does OSSN have?

    _____

Name

Date

Directions: Consider the following concepts and issues. Conduct research to help you respond, and be prepared to discuss the topic in class.

Mission Statements

Creating a mission statement is one of the first tasks you should perform during the planning stages of your new business. A mission statement defines the purpose of your business. Your mission statement should be a clear, concise statement that says what your agency is, what it does, for whom, and where. In just one or two sentences, a mission statement needs to communicate the unique essence of your company.

1. Conduct research on the Internet on how to write a mission statement.

2. Visit a number of travel agency Web sites, and read each of their mission statements. List three mission statements you feel are well-written.

   a. Company _____

      Mission _____

      _____

   b. Company _____

      Mission _____

      _____

   c. Company _____

      Mission _____

      _____

3. Write a mission statement for a home-based travel agency (specialty of your choice).

   _____

   _____

   _____

   _____

Name _____   Date _____

Directions: Define the following terms.

1. Application letter _____

_____

2. CHRIE _____

_____

3. Cover letter _____

_____

4. Networking _____

_____

5. Résumé _____

_____

Name _____   Date _____

Directions: Conduct a self-assessment. For each of the following categories, list your qualifications and qualities.

1. Skills _____

   _____

   _____

2. Knowledge _____

   _____

   _____

3. Talents _____

   _____

   _____

4. Interests _____

   _____

   _____

5. Personal preferences _____

   _____

   _____

6. Accomplishments _____

   _____

   _____

Directions: Choose a position in the travel industry that interests you. (You might want to look again at Table 1.1 on page 14 in the textbook.) Now assume that you have been scheduled for an interview for that position. How would you answer the following questions during the interview?

7. What is it about this position that interests you?

   _____

8. What do you see yourself doing five years from now?

   _____

(continued)

9. Tell me about two achievements of which you are most proud.

   _____

   _____

10. Give an example of a major problem you faced and how you solved it.

    _____

    _____

11. What is your greatest accomplishment?

    _____

    _____

12. Of all your jobs, which did you like best? Why?

    _____

    _____

13. Which job did you like least? Why?

    _____

    _____

14. If you could have made two improvements in your last job, what would they have been?

    _____

    _____

15. Why should you be my first choice for this position?

    _____

    _____

16. What five words best describe you?

    _____

    _____

Worksheet 15.3 Résumé Worksheet

Name _____ Date _____

Directions: Fill in this worksheet to use as a reference for your résumé.

Name _____

Address _____

Telephone (home) _____

Telephone (business) _____

Fax _____

E-mail _____

Career objective _____

Education (List the most recent school first.) _____

Dates attended: From _____ to _____

Degree or diploma earned _____

Major and Minor subjects _____

Awards, honors, certificates _____

(Repeat the preceding section for each school attended after high school.)

High School _____

Dates attended: From _____ to _____

Diploma earned Yes _____ No _____

Work Experience (List the most recent job first.)

Name of firm _____

Address _____

Dates of employment: From _____ to _____

Title _____

Duties _____

Special achievements (awards, citations, commendations, promotions, etc.) _____

(continued)

(Repeat the preceding section for each position held.)

Military experience _____

Related outside interests _____

_____

_____

Travels _____

_____

_____

References (on separate sheet) _____

_____

_____

1. On separate paper, write your résumé using the information from this worksheet, from Worksheet 15.2, and from Figures 15.2 (page 368) and 15.3 (page 369) in the textbook. (Your résumé worksheet is a reference guide so that you have information handy; don't let it dictate what you emphasize in your résumé. Your self-assessment in Worksheet 15.2 may be more important.)

2. On separate paper, write a cover letter that would be appropriate to apply for the position you selected in question 7 on Worksheet 15.2.

Name _____   Date _____

Directions: Answer the following questions.

1. What are the distinguishing characteristics of the following types of travel positions?

   a. Nonpersonal phone work _____

   _____

   b. Personal intermediary of services _____

   _____

   c. In-person supplier of services _____

   _____

2. What are four key items that employers look for on an application or résumé?

   a. _____

   b. _____

   c. _____

   d. _____

3. What are three things you should do to prepare for an interview?

   a. _____

   b. _____

   c. _____

4. What are five sources of information about employment opportunities?

   a. _____

   b. _____

   c. _____

   d. _____

   e. _____

(continued)

Directions: Indicate whether each of the following statements is true or false. If a statement is false, explain why.

5. You should listen carefully for an opportunity to ask for a job during an information interview. True or false?

   _____

6. You should always accompany a résumé with a cover letter. True or false?

   _____

7. If you are offered two jobs, always take the one with the higher salary when you are starting without experience. True or false?

   _____

8. Positions for travel counselors are found in every area of the country. True or false?

   _____

9. Positions for airline reservationists are found in every area of the country. True or false?

   _____

10. When you have an interview, find out how people dress in that office and dress accordingly. True or false?

   _____

11. You should be a half-hour early for an interview to make sure you are on time. True or false?

   _____

Name   Date

Directions: Practice using the Web to help in a job search by completing the following exercises.

1. Go to the "Careers" section at the bottom of the Web site for Choice Hotels (www.choicehotels.com), and then click on "Locations." Choose one position listed at the site; note the position and where the job is located.

   _____

2. Go to the employment opportunity section of American Airlines' Web site (www.aa.com), and list at least one job currently available.

   _____

3. Look for employment opportunities listed at the Web site of Hertz Corporation (www.hertz.com). Note an entry-level position at a location near you.

   _____

4. Go to the job listing site, Monster (www.monster.com). Enter "hospitality tourism" in the "Keyword" box under "Quick Search" and your Zip code to find jobs in your geographical area. Note one job that you might want in the future. (Most job listings are for people with experience.)

   _____

5. Go to www.monster.com and examine the tips on résumés, interviews, and other job-finding skills. List one tip that you would like to share with other students.

   _____

   _____

6. Go to www.yoursintravel.com, which focuses on travel jobs for candidates with experience. List one job that you might want in the future.

   _____

7. Go to www.jobhuntersbible.com, and list three Web sites for job searches that you had not been familiar with.

   _____

   _____

   _____

Name   Date

Directions: Consider the following concepts and issues. First fill in the weaknesses, and then list the corresponding strengths.

Weaknesses = Overextensions of Strengths

The dreaded interview question almost always comes, "What are your weaknesses?" You know that you can't say, "I have no weaknesses," but which of your weaknesses won't seem so negative? Human nature is such that it is much easier for us to identify our weaknesses than it is for us to define our strengths.

It has been said, "Our weaknesses are merely overextensions of our strengths."
Do you agree with that philosophy? Try it for yourself by completing the following exercise.

Weakness   **Strength**
example: *example:*
Stubborn   Determined, sees projects through to completion

_____

_____

_____

_____

_____

_____

_____

_____

_____

_____

_____

_____

_____

_____

_____

_____

_____

Name   Date

Directions: Define the following terms.

1. Back-to-back ticketing _____

   _____

2. Corporate culture _____

   _____

3. Doublebooking _____

   _____

4. Hidden-city ticketing _____

   _____

5. Mentor _____

   _____

6. Professional _____

   _____

Designations and Certifications

Directions: Define the following terms.

1. ACC _____

   _____

2. CITE _____

   _____

3. CMP _____

   _____

4. CTA _____

   _____

5. CTC _____

   _____

(continued)

6. CTP _____

_____

7. Destination Specialist _____

_____

8. DMC _____

_____

9. MCC _____

_____

10. TAP Test _____

_____

Name   Date

Directions: Read the following hypothetical situations, and choose the response that best reflects your judgment of what is ethical.

1. One of the car rental companies that you frequently recommend is giving laptop computers to travel agents who book 50 clients in one month. You need only one more booking to win, and it's the last day of the month. Just in time, a corporate traveler calls. When you suggest the car rental company that is offering the laptop, he says that he would prefer another company.

   What do you do? Circle a, b, or c.

   a. Tell the client that your agency has had favorable dealings with the company in question, that you recommend it highly, and then let him decide.

   b. Explain why that company is his only option and book him anyway.

   c. Book the client with the company of his preference and hope that someone else will call so you can win the laptop.

   What were the reasons and ethical principles that guided your selection?

   _____

   _____

   _____

2. After you have spent three hours researching and booking a high-commission European vacation, your client calls to say that she wants you to transfer this reservation to another agency. When you ask her why, she says that she likes it better and that it is located closer to her home. Although you offer to deliver her tickets, vouchers, and any other information she may need, she still wants you to switch agencies. You know that you reserved the last two seats on her departing flight, and if you don't release her seats to the other agency, she probably won't be able to rebook.

   What do you do? Circle a, b, or c.

   a. Refuse to release, telling her it's against company policy (whether your agency has such a rule or not).

   b. Tell her you'll release. But cancel all her bookings after you hang up.

   c. Release the reservation.

   What were the reasons and ethical principles that guided your selection?

   _____

   _____

   _____

(continued)

3. Your best friend has always dreamed of taking a Caribbean cruise. She knows about familiarization (fam) trips and how cheaply you can sometimes travel on them. Please, she asks, can you book her on one of those trips? All it will take is a request on travel agency letterhead saying that she is an employee. She's a longtime friend who has done special favors for you in the past.

   What do you do? Circle a, b, or c.

   a. Book her on an upcoming cruise as long as she promises not to tell anybody that she's not really a travel agent.

   b. Tell her you're sorry, but you could lose your job if you got caught.

   c. Offer to find her an economical cruise she can afford instead of a fam trip.

   What were the reasons and ethical principles that guided your selection?

   _____

   _____

   _____

4. You've been offered a better salary and an opportunity for rapid advancement at a new agency. You accept. But alone in the office one evening, before you've given notice to your current employer, you realize that it would be easy to copy your agency's client list from your computer without anyone finding out. The list would help show your new boss that you know how to generate business.

   What do you do? Circle a, b, or c.

   a. Copy the list.

   b. Copy only the names of the clients you know are coming with you anyway.

   c. Decide not to copy anything, even though you're not particularly fond of your current boss.

   What were the reasons and ethical principles that guided your selection?

   _____

   _____

   _____

Name _____ Date _____

Directions: For each of the following skills, list a position within the travel and tourism industry in which that skill would be useful, and describe how the skill could be applied to that position. (Describing a situation or explaining how the skill could be used will be especially helpful.)

1. Organizational skills

   a. Position _____

   b. How can this skill be applied to the position you chose?

   _____

2. Time management skills

   a. Position _____

   b. How can this skill be applied to the position you chose?

   _____

3. Negotiating skills

   a. Position _____

   b. How can this skill be applied to the position you chose?

   _____

4. Understanding consumer trends and customer motivations

   a. Position _____

   b. How can this skill be applied to the position you chose?

   _____

5. Crisis management skills

   a. Position _____

   b. How can this skill be applied to the position you chose?

   _____

6. Business communication skills

   a. Position _____

   b. How can this skill be applied to the position you chose?

   _____

(continued)

7. Cultural diversity skills

   a. Position _____

   b. How can this skill be applied to the position you chose?

   _____

Name   Date

Directions: Indicate whether each of the following statements is true or false. If it is false, explain why.

1. A good way to be successful on your new job is to do only what you are told so you don't get into trouble taking the initiative on tasks you have not yet learned. True or false?

   _____

2. A good way to be successful on your new job is to act as if you know the answers to most questions (especially with clients) even if you don't. True or false?

   _____

3. A good way to be successful on your new job is to find a person in the company whom you can emulate. True or false?

   _____

4. A good way to be successful on your new job is to help colleagues when necessary but avoid doing too much so that you aren't taken advantage of. True or false?

   _____

5. A good way to be successful on your new job is to tread softly in suggesting that changes be made until you have been with the company for awhile. True or false?

   _____

6. Following the corporate culture means obeying each rule and policy of the office to the letter. True or false?

   _____

Directions: Provide the information requested in the following exercises.

7. Describe five steps to move up the career ladder.

   a. _____

   b. _____

   c. _____

   d. _____

   e. _____

(continued)

8. List seven skills that are important for travel professionals to develop.

   a. _____

   b. _____

   c. _____

   d. _____

   e. _____

   f. _____

   g. _____

9. Describe how successful professionals approach change and why it is important to have a strategy to manage change in the travel industry.

10. Describe the ethical principle of confidentiality.

   _____

   _____

11. List three logical steps you might take to develop a specialization.

   a. _____

   b. _____

   c. _____

12. If you worked in a travel agency and were given the opportunity to specialize, what field would you choose? Describe two ways that you could promote your specialty to potential customers.

   _____

   _____

   _____

   _____

   _____

   _____

Name   Date

Directions: Complete the following exercises for practice using the Web to find information to help you build your career.

1. Go to www.thetravelinstitute.com, and find information about the TAP test.

   a. What is the test location that is most convenient for you?

   _____

   b. Is the TAP Test available online?

   _____

   c. What are three advantages or benefits of taking and passing the TAP Test?

   _____

   _____

2. Go to ASTA's Web site and click on the "Education & Careers" section. List one of the seminars, events, or specialty courses that would help you to advance your career.

   _____

3. Look at the fam trips offered at www.ossn.com. List one that you might enjoy or that might enhance your career.

   _____

4. Click on the "Rules of the Air" section at www.onetravel.com. Choose an airline and a subject category to find one controversial subject. Summarize the advice about this subject in a sentence or two.

   _____

   _____

   _____

5. Choose a course that looks interesting under "Distance Learning" at the "Educational Institute" section on the Web site of the American Hotel & Lodging Association (www.ahma.com).

   _____

6. Go to CLIA's Web site (www.cruising.org), and list a seminar or course that might enhance your career. (You may have to search a bit to find CLIA's course offerings. Try clicking on "Travel Agents.")

   _____

(continued)

7. Go to the Association of Destination Management Executive's Web site. Describe its mission and list three ways it plans to reach this goal.

   Mission _____

   Methods used to reach its mission

   a. _____

   b. _____

   c. _____

8. Go to NTA's Web site. Find the checklist titled "Avoiding Travel Scams." List three tips on this checklist.

   a. _____

   b. _____

   c. _____

9. Find scholarship information on the CHRIE Web site. What is the section's URL?

   _____

10. Go to the guest section of SITE's Web site. When is their next convention and where will it be held?

    _____

Name   Date

Directions: Consider the following concepts and issues. Conduct research to help you respond, and be prepared to discuss the topic in class. (Tip: Refer to the Web sites listed in the "Resources: On Building a Career" section on page 399 of Chapter 16 of the *Travel Career Development* textbook and other resources.)

Global Code of Ethics for Tourism

The Global Code of Ethics for Tourism (GCET) is a comprehensive set of principles whose purpose is to guide the stakeholders in tourism development: central and local governments, local communities, the tourism industry and its professionals, as well as international and domestic visitors.

Find the set of principles along with their corresponding articles (on the WTO's Web site).

Choose one of the ten articles; explain its purpose and what actions are required by the stakeholders named above to adhere to the principle. Write a one-page report on your findings, and be prepared to discuss the topic in class.

Article # _____

Article statement _____

Purpose of Principle _____

_____

Explain the actions that can be taken by each responsible party (stakeholders in tourism development, governments, host communities, travel professionals, and/or tourists) to adhere to this principle.

_____

_____

_____

_____

_____

_____

_____

_____

_____

_____

_____

_____

Name   Date

Directions: Answer the following questions.

1. In which state will you find the Finger Lakes, Lake Champlain, and Lake George?

_____

2. Williamsburg is in which state?

_____

3. What is Branson, Missouri, famous for?

_____

4. In which state will you find Portland, Mt. Hood, and Columbia Gorge?

_____

5. What city is home to the Mormon Tabernacle?

_____

6. To which state would you travel to visit the pueblos of the Southwest?

_____

7. Where is Mt. Rushmore?

_____

8. Which city is known for cable cars and the Golden Gate Bridge?

_____

9. Which state consists of an Upper and a Lower Peninsula?

_____

10. Where is the Grand Canyon?

_____

11. Which Canadian provinces are known as the Maritime provinces?

_____

12. What city is home to the CN Tower?

_____

(continued)

13. What Canadian city is known for its flower gardens, Parliament buildings, and famous Empress Hotel?

_____

14. What is the capital of Canada?

_____

15. Where is Disney World? Disneyland?

_____

Directions: Using the atlas at the end of *Travel Career Development* and any other reference material you need, answer the following questions.

16. What body of water must you cross to go from Bar Harbor, Maine, to Yarmouth, Nova Scotia?

_____

17. What body of water must you cross to go from New Orleans, Louisiana, to Cairo, Mississippi?

_____

18. Great Smoky Mountains National Park extends through which states?

_____

19. What is the latitude and longitude of your city?

_____

Name _____   Date _____

Directions: Answer the following questions.

1. What are the three primary resort areas of Jamaica?

   a. _____

   b. _____

   c. _____

2. What three Caribbean islands are known as the ABC islands?

   a. _____

   b. _____

   c. _____

3. What is the main attraction of Chichén Itzá, Tulum, and Uxmal?

   _____

4. What part of Mexico is home to the great pyramids?

   _____

5. What are the two large groups into which the Caribbean islands are often classified?

   a. _____

   b. _____

6. What three islands make up the U.S. Virgin Islands?

   a. _____

   b. _____

   c. _____

7. Bermuda is in what ocean?

   _____

8. What are the two most popular tourist centers in the Bahamas?

   a. _____

   b. _____

(continued)

9. What are two popular resorts of Mexico, and which coasts are they on?

    a. _____

    b. _____

Directions: Using the atlas at the back of *Travel Career Development* and any other reference material you need, answer the following questions.

10. What body of water must you cross to go from Tampa, Florida, to Cancún, Mexico?

    _____

11. What are the names of the British Virgin Islands?

    _____

    _____

Name   Date

Directions: Answer the following questions.

1. What are the seven countries of Central America?

   a. _____   e. _____

   b. _____   f. _____

   c. _____   g. _____

   d. _____

2. What is the highest capital city in the world?

   _____

3. To what country do the Galápagos Islands belong, and where are they?

   _____

4. What complex built by the Incas is one of the most popular tourist attractions in Peru?

   _____

5. Where is Angel Falls, the highest waterfall in the world?

   _____

6. What Argentinean city is famous for its wide boulevards and large parks?

   _____

7. What Brazilian city is noted for its sculpture of Christ the Redeemer, its Mardi Gras, and its beaches?

   _____

Directions: Using the atlas at the end of *Travel Career Development* and any other reference material you need, answer the following questions.

8. What is a popular ski resort in Argentina?

   _____

9. What city in Brazil is a stop on Amazon River cruises?

   _____

Name   Date

Directions: Answer the following questions.

1. What countries make up Benelux?

   _____

2. What countries occupy the Iberian Peninsula?

   _____

3. What countries are on the British Isles?

   _____

4. In what countries would you find the Alps?

   _____

5. Where is Salzburg, and what is it famous for?

   _____

6. Safari tours to Africa often focus on the game parks of Amboseli and Masai Mara in what country?

   _____

7. Where are the Temples of Karnak and Luxor?

   _____

Directions: Name the city in which you would find the following attractions.

8. The Parthenon   _____

9. The Colosseum   _____

10. The Louvre   _____

Directions: Using the atlas at the end of *Travel Career Development* and any other reference material you need, answer the following questions.

11. What body of water must you cross to go from Capetown, South Africa, to the Seychelles Islands?

    _____

12. What body of water must you cross to go from Venice, Italy, to Athens, Greece?

    _____

(continued)

13. What body of water must you cross to go from Rome, Italy, to Malta?

    _____

14. What body of water must you cross to go from Edinburgh, Scotland, to Hamburg, Germany?

    _____

15. If someone wants to visit Timbuktu, to what country would you send this person?

    _____

16. What is the largest island in the Mediterranean?

    _____

17. The westernmost capital city in Europe lies on seven low hills at the estuary north of the river Tagus. What is the city?

    _____

Name   Date

Directions: Answer the following questions.

1. What is the capital of Thailand and the home of nearly 400 Buddhist temples?

   _____

2. What is the name of one the most famous tombs in the world, located in Agra, India?

   _____

3. What is the sacred mountain of Japan, the traditional destination of pilgrimages?

   _____

4. What city in China is the site of an emperor's tomb that includes an army of life-size terra cotta soldiers?

   _____

5. What city would you visit to see the Summer Palace, Imperial Palace, and Forbidden City?

   _____

6. What city is known for its Opera House, Harbour Bridge, and the Rocks?

   _____

7. What are some animals native only to Australia?

   _____

8. What is the name of the native people of New Zealand?

   _____

9. What are three of the islands in each of the following island groups?

   a. Polynesia   _____

                                  _____

   b. Melanesia   _____

                                  _____

   c. Micronesia   _____

                                  _____

(continued)

Directions: Using the atlas at the end of *Travel Career Development* and any other reference material you need, answer the following questions.

10. What body of water must you cross to go from Perth, Australia, to Bombay, India?

    _____

11. What body of water must you cross to go from Singapore to Manila, Philippines?

    _____

12. What European country was the first to establish permanent settlements in Australia and New Zealand?

    _____

Name   Date

Directions: Answer the following questions.

1. Tours near the North Pole or the South Pole may bring adventurers to what destinations?

_____

2. Greenland is a possession of what country?

_____

3. What country or countries own Antarctica?

_____

4. Gateways used to reach Greenland include what countries?

_____

5. Travelers can travel by ship to Antarctica via what gateway cities?

_____

Name   Date

Directions: Use the Web to answer the following questions about destinations around the world. (Tip: You can find answers to some of the questions on maps. For most of the other questions, try the Web sites of tourist offices. To find the official Web sites of tourist offices around the world, you may want to access The Tourism Offices Worldwide Directory at www.towd.com.)

1. What city is located at 140 degrees east longitude and 36 degrees north latitude?

   _____

2. Through what countries in the Western Hemisphere does the Tropic of Cancer pass?

   _____

   _____

3. Scotland's tourist board divides the country into how many regions in its "Guide to Scotland"?

   _____

4. One of Thailand's mottoes is "Welcome to the Land of _____ ."

   _____

5. What is the Pantanal, and where is it found?

   _____

6. According to the "Getting Here" section of Prince Edward Island's tourism Web site, how many miles is it from New York City to Prince Edward Island?

   _____

7. What are the six major Norwegian cities listed on the Web site of its tourist office?

   _____

   _____

   _____

8. How many national parks are listed on New Zealand's Web site?

   _____

9. Where is the Blue Mosque?

   _____

10. Where is the Uffizi Gallery?

   _____

(continued)

11. What tourist attraction in Northern Ireland is a complex of thousands of hexagonal basalt columns?

_____

12. What mountains form the backbone of Italy?

_____

13. Where does the White Nile join the Blue Nile?

_____

14. Where is Canada's first national park, Banff, located?

_____

15. What famous lake is shared by Italy and Switzerland?

_____

16. What sea on the Israeli-Jordanian border is the lowest point on the surface of the earth?

_____

17. For what is the Romantic Road in Germany famous?

_____

Part 2:
Resources

An Amtrak Timetable

Monday through Friday Service (Will not operate 5/28 or 7/4)

Train Number ▶		201	101	103	105	107	2153	2155	111	113	115	117	119	2183	121	123	125	2171	127	2175
Boston, MA–South Sta	Dp						6 12A	7 12A										3 12P		5 12P
Boston, MA–Back Bay							R 6 17A	R 7 17A										R 3 17P		R 5 17P
Route 128, MA							R 6 26A	R 7 26A										R 3 26P		R 5 26P
Providence, RI							6 47A	7 47A										3 47P		5 47P
New Haven, CT ✳	Ar						8 18A	9 18A										5 18P		7 18P
New York, NY ✳	Ar						9 40A	10 42A										6 42P		8 42P
New York, NY ✳	Dp	5 25A	6 00A	7 00A	8 00A	9 00A	10 00A		11 00A	12 00N	1 00P	2 00P	3 00P	3 50P	4 00P	5 00P	6 00P		7 00P	9 00P
Newark, NJ		R 5 40A	R 6 15A	R 7 15A	R 8 15A	R 9 15A			R11 15A	R12 15P	R 1 15P	R 2 15P	R 3 15P		R 4 15P	R 5 15P	R 6 15P		R 7 15P	9 13P
Metropark, NJ		5 52A	6 27A	7 27A	8 27A	9 27A			11 27A			2 27P				5 27P				
Princeton Jct., NJ		6 10A	6 45A																	
Trenton, NJ		6 20A	6 54A																	9 42P
Philadelphia, PA ✳	Ar	6 51A	7 25A	8 14A	9 14A	10 14A	11 05A		12 14P	1 11P	2 11P	3 14P	4 11P	4 52P	5 14P	6 14P	7 11P		8 11P	10 08P
Wilmington, DE		7 13A	7 46A	8 35A	9 35A	10 35A	11 25A		12 35P	1 32P	2 32P	3 35P	4 32P		5 35P	6 35P	7 32P		8 32P	10 28P
Baltimore, MD		7 59A	8 31A	9 21A	10 21A	11 21A	12 05P		1 21P	2 18P	3 18P	4 21P	5 18P		6 21P	7 21P	8 18P		9 18P	11 08P
BWI Air. Rail Sta., MD Ⓐ		8 12A		9 34A	10 34A	11 34A	12 17P		1 34P	2 31P	3 31P	4 34P	5 31P		6 34P	7 34P	8 31P		9 31P	11 20P
New Carrollton, MD			D 8 53A							D 2 44P	D 3 44P	D 4 47P	D 5 44P		D 6 47P	D 7 47P	D 8 44P		D 9 44P	
Washington, DC ✳	Ar	8 33A	9 05A	9 59A	10 59A	11 59A	12 44P		1 59P	2 59P	3 59P	4 59P	5 59P	6 20P	6 59P	7 59P	8 59P		9 59P	11 44P

Weekend Service (Will also operate 5/28 and 7/4)

Train Number ▶		205	207	209	211	2253	215	219	221	223	225	2273
Days of Operation ▶		Sa Ⓢ	Su Ⓤ	SaSu	Su Ⓤ	SaSu	SaSu	SaSu	Su Ⓤ	Su Ⓤ	SaSu	SaSu
Boston, MA–South Sta	Dp					8 00A						4 00P
Boston, MA–Back Bay						R 8 05A						R 4 05P
Route 128, MA						R 8 14A						R 4 14P
Providence, RI						8 35A						4 35P
New Haven, CT ✳	Ar					10 18A						6 18P
New York, NY ✳	Ar					11 42A						7 42P
New York, NY ✳	Dp	8 00A	9 00A	10 00A	11 00A	12 00N	1 00P	3 00P	4 00P	5 00P	6 00P	8 00P
Newark, NJ		R 8 15A	R 9 15A	R10 15A	R11 15A		R 1 15P	R 3 15P	R 4 15P	R 5 15P	R 6 15P	8 13P
Metropark, NJ		8 27A	9 27A	10 27A	11 27A		1 27P	3 27P	4 27P	5 27P	6 27P	
Princeton Jct., NJ												
Trenton, NJ												8 25P
Philadelphia, PA ✳	Ar	9 14A	10 14A	11 14A	12 14P	12 13P	2 14P	4 14P	5 14P	6 14P	7 14P	9 10P
Wilmington, DE		9 35A	10 35A	11 35A	12 35P		2 35P	4 35P	5 35P	6 35P	7 35P	9 30P
Baltimore, MD		10 21A	11 21A	12 21P	1 21P		3 21P	5 21P	6 21P	7 21P	8 21P	10 10P
BWI Air. Rail Sta., MD Ⓐ		10 34A	11 34A	12 34P	1 34P		3 34P	5 34P	6 34P	7 34P	8 34P	10 22P
New Carrollton, MD		D10 47A	D11 47A	D12 47P	D 1 47P		D 3 47P	D 5 47P	D 6 47P	D 7 47P	D 8 47P	
Washington, DC ✳	Ar	11 04A	12 04P	1 04P	2 04P	2 50P	4 04P	6 04P	7 04P	8 04P	9 04P	10 50P

Services on Metroliner and Acela Express Trains

All trains offer sandwich, snack and beverage service Railfone® On-board Telephone Service and First Class service. All trains are reserved. Reserved seat ticket required for boarding. Smoking is not permitted on these trains.

A   Time Symbol for A.M.   P   Time Symbol for P.M.   N   Time Symbol for Noon.

D   Stops only to discharge passengers; train may leave ahead of schedule when station work is completed.

R   Stops only to receive passengers.

✳   Amtrak Vacations package (s) available at this destination. Book your hotel and/or tour by calling 1-800-321-8684.

Free shuttle service between rail and air terminal.

Ⓢ   Will also operate 5/27.

Ⓤ   Will not operate 5/27.

Shading indicates Acela Express.

For Metroliner® and Acela Express℠ reservations and information, call 1-800-USA-RAIL or your travel agent, or visit www.amtrak.com on the Internet.

Amtrak® is a registered service mark of the National Railroad Passenger Corporation.

Form W9/140M   Stock No. 023094   Schedules subject to change without notice.

Source: Reprinted by permission of Amtrak. © 2002 Amtrak.

Fares & Schedules

Rail Map

Home | Rail | Air | Car | Hotel | EuroGroups | Destination | About Us | FAQ | E-mail | Site Map | View Shopping Cart

Rail Europe
Fares &
Schedules
**Single Country
Passes**
**Multiple
Country Passes**
**Rail 'n Drive
Passes**
Youth Passes

Travel Resources
**All About Train
Travel**
**About
Reservations**

AVE
Eurostar
Talgo
TGV Med
Thalys
**Trainhotel
Elipsos**
**All Premier
Trains**

From London, Britain to Paris, France

From London to Paris direct

BOOK NOW   Please read the <u>terms and conditions</u>.

From	London Waterloo
To	Paris Nord
Route Effective	4/1/2002 to 6/15/2002
Fare Effective	1/1/2002 to 1/3/2003
Time	03:00
Distance	494 km / 308 mi

Reservations on this train are mandatory and included in the cost of the ticket.

Fares

Fill in the number of passengers for each desired fare category and choose the class of travel. Click on a fare category below for conditions of use.

Number of Passengers	Fare Category	First Class	Second Class
☐	<u>Child</u>	$109.00 ⦿	$69.00 ○
☐	<u>First Premium</u>	$399.00 ⦿	N/A
☐	<u>Full Fare</u>	$279.00 ⦿	$199.00 ○
☐	<u>Leisure RT 14 Business Days Advance*</u>	N/A	$89.00 ⦿
☐	<u>Leisure RT 65 Days Advance**</u>	N/A	$60.00 ⦿
☐	<u>Leisure</u>	$219.00 ⦿	$139.00 ○
☐	<u>Passholder</u>	$155.00 ⦿	$75.00 ○

Source: Pages reprinted by permission of Rail Europe, www.raileurope.com.

Rail Europe Fares and Schedules *(continued)*

☐	Senior	$189.00 ⊙	N/A	
☐	Wheelchair adult	$54.00 ⊙	N/A	
☐	Wheelchair child	$43.00 ⊙	N/A	
☐	Wheelchair Companion	$54.00 ⊙	$54.00 ○	
☐	Youth	$165.00 ⊙	$79.00 ○	

Note: * Leisure RT 14 Business Days Advance must be purchased at least 14 business days before date of travel and is subject to availability. A minimum 2-night stay is required. A return ticket must be booked to receive these fares. Fares are per person, one-way.

** Leisure RT 65 Days Advance must be purchased at least 65 days before date of travel and is subject to availability. A minimum 2-night stay is required. A return ticket must be booked to receive these fares. Fares are per person, one-way.

Schedules

Select a time from the following table.

Select	Dep. Time	Arr. Time	Destination	Train #	Notes
⊙	05:15	09:23	Paris	9078-ERS	Monday-Friday
○	06:19	10:23	Paris	9002-ERS	Monday-Saturday
○	06:53	10:59	Paris	9004-ERS	Saturday only
○	07:23	11:23	Paris	9006-ERS	Monday-Saturday
○	07:53	11:47	Paris	9008-ERS	Saturday only
○	08:10	12:23	Paris	9010-ERS	Daily
○	08:43	12:53	Paris	9012-ERS	Fri, Sat & Sun
○	09:23	13:23	Paris	9014-ERS	Monday-Friday

○	09:53	13:53	Paris	9016-ERS	Saturday only
○	10:10	14:17	Paris	9018-ERS	Daily
○	11:43	15:59	Paris	9024-ERS	Daily
○	12:43	16:47	Paris	9028-ERS	Daily
○	13:10	17:23	Paris	9030-ERS	Sunday only
○	13:43	17:53	Paris	9032-ERS	Daily
○	15:10	19:23	Paris	9038-ERS	Daily
○	15:43	19:47	Paris	9040-ERS	Fri & Sun only
○	16:10	20:23	Paris	9042-ERS	Daily
○	16:48	20:59	Paris	9044-ERS	Please Call
○	17:10	21:23	Paris	9046-ERS	Except Saturday
○	17:43	21:53	Paris	9048-ERS	Sat & Sun
○	18:10	22:23	Paris	9050-ERS	Except Saturday
○	18:43	22:53	Paris	9052-ERS	Sunday only
○	19:10	23:23	Paris	9054-ERS	Daily
○	19:43	23:47	Paris	9056-ERS	Sunday only

Legend
Train Codes: ERS: EUROSTAR

EUROSTAR SERVICE: All times are local. Continental Europe is 1 hr ahead of Great Britain..

A Thomas Cook Timetable

Table 44 — LONDON - PARIS - TORINO - MILANO - VENEZIA and ROMA

train type	EC	IC	IC	TGV	CIS	P	TGV	IC	IC	IR	IC	IC	IC	☆	TGV	IC	IC		IR	IC	P	P
train number	142/3	521	503	EC21	35	9521	EC17	623	585	2051	345	555	525	9078	EC19	1507	627	805	2109	637	9417	9419
London Waterloo 10 ★ d.	…	…	…	…	…	…	…	…	…	…	…	…	…	0550	…	…	…	…	…	…	…	…
Paris Nord 10 ★ a.	…	…	…	…	…	…	…	…	…	…	…	…	…	1014	…	…	…	…	…	…	…	…
Paris Gare de Lyon d.	…	…	…	0712	…	…	0818	…	…	…	…	…	…	…	1118	…	…	…	…	…	…	…
Dijon d.	…	…	…	0853	…	…	…	…	…	…	…	…	…	…	…	…	…	…	…	…	…	…
Lyon Perrache d.	0708	…	…	…	…	…	…	…	…	…	…	…	…	…	…	…	…	…	…	…	…	…
Lyon Part Dieu d.	0720	…	…	…	…	…	…	…	…	…	…	…	1243	…	…	…	…	…	…	…	…	…
Chambéry d.	0840	…	…	…	…	…	1110	…	…	…	…	…	1403	…	1413	…	…	…	…	…	…	…
Modane d.	0944	…	…	…	…	…	1216	…	…	…	…	…	…	…	1516	…	…	…	…	…	…	…
Vallorbe d.	…	…	…	1034	…	…	…	…	…	…	…	…	…	…	…	…	…	…	…	…	…	…
Lausanne a.	…	…	…	1106	1113	…	…	…	…	…	…	…	…	…	…	…	…	…	…	…	…	…
Domodossola § a.	…	…	…	…	1304	…	…	…	…	…	…	…	…	…	…	…	…	…	…	…	…	…
Stresa a.	…	…	…	…	…	…	…	…	…	…	…	…	…	…	…	…	…	…	…	…	…	…
Arona a.	…	…	…	…	1327	…	…	…	…	…	…	…	…	…	…	…	…	…	…	…	…	…
Oulx a.	1009	…	…	…	…	…	1241	…	…	…	…	…	…	…	1541	…	…	…	…	…	…	…
Torino Porta Susa a.	…	…	…	…	…	…	1327	…	…	…	…	…	…	…	1627	…	…	…	…	…	…	…
Torino Porta Nuova a.	1058	1110	1115	…	…	…	…	…	…	…	1425	…	…	…	…	…	…	1805	…	…	…	…
Novara a.	…	…	1216	…	…	…	…	…	…	1418	…	…	…	…	1718	…	…	…	…	…	…	…
Milano Centrale a.	…	…	1250	…	1420	1455	1450	1505	1505	…	1510	1600	…	…	1750	1805	1810	…	1815	1905	1930	1940
Genova Piazza Principe a.	…	1246	…	…	…	…	…	…	1611	…	1649	…	…	…	…	…	1941	1952	…	…	…	…
Rapallo a.	…	…	…	…	…	…	…	…	1647	…	1719	…	…	…	…	…	…	2015	…	…	…	…
La Spezia a.	…	1355	…	…	…	…	…	…	1734	…	1755	…	…	…	…	…	2106	2122	…	…	…	…
Viareggio a.	…	1428	…	…	…	…	…	…	1816	…	1828	…	…	…	…	…	…	…	…	…	…	…
Pisa Centrale a.	…	1445	…	…	…	…	…	…	1835	…	1845	…	…	…	…	…	2210	…	…	…	…	…
Livorno a.	…	1501	…	…	…	…	…	…	…	…	1901	…	…	…	…	…	2226	…	…	…	…	…
Grosseto a.	…	1609	…	…	…	…	…	…	…	…	2009	…	…	…	…	…	2340	…	…	…	…	…
Verona a.	…	…	…	…	…	…	…	1630	…	…	…	…	…	…	…	1935	…	…	1959	2030	…	…
Padova a.	…	…	…	…	…	…	…	1721	…	…	…	…	…	…	…	2026	…	…	2058	2121	…	…
Venezia Mestre a.	…	…	…	…	…	…	…	1743	…	…	…	…	…	…	…	2048	…	…	2119	2143	…	…
Venezia Santa Lucia a.	…	…	…	…	…	…	…	1755	…	…	…	…	…	…	…	2100	…	…	2130	2155	…	…
Bologna Centrale a.	…	…	…	…	…	1633	…	…	…	1656	…	1747	…	…	…	…	…	…	…	…	…	2118
Rimini a.	…	…	…	…	…	…	…	…	…	1803	…	…	…	…	…	…	…	…	…	…	…	…
Ancona a.	…	…	…	…	…	…	…	…	…	1859	…	…	…	…	…	…	…	…	…	…	…	…
Pescara Centrale a.	…	…	…	…	…	…	…	…	…	2029	…	…	…	…	…	…	…	…	…	…	…	…
Bari Centrale a.	…	…	…	…	…	…	…	…	…	2330	…	…	…	…	…	…	…	…	…	…	…	…
Brindisi Centrale a.	…	…	…	…	…	…	…	…	…	…	…	…	…	…	…	…	…	…	…	…	…	…
Patras 2770 a.	…	…	…	…	…	…	…	…	…	…	…	…	…	…	…	…	…	…	…	…	…	…
Athinai 2770 a.	…	…	…	…	…	…	…	…	…	…	…	…	…	…	…	…	…	…	…	…	…	…
Firenze SMN a.	…	…	…	…	…	1732	…	…	…	…	…	1852	…	…	…	…	…	…	…	…	…	2210r
Roma Termini a.	…	1755	…	…	…	1915	…	…	…	…	…	2055	2155	…	…	…	…	…	…	…	2325	2350
Napoli Centrale 370 a.	…	…	…	…	…	…	…	…	…	…	…	2300	…	…	…	…	…	…	…	…	…	…

train type	☆	TGV	IC	IC	TGV	EC	IC	IC	☆	TGV	CIS	TGV	EC	☆	EN	EN	EN	IC	215/219	215/219	IC	☆	EN	IC
train number	9004	EC23	335	645	613	146/7	529	509	9016	EC29	37	659	138/9	9032	213	223	215	571	219	219	515	9040	217	575
notes															L	R	G		V	W		S		
London Waterloo 10 ★ d.	0657n	…	…	…	…	…	…	…	0953c	…	…	…	…	1357n	…	…	…	…	…	…	1553c	…	…	…
Paris Nord 10 ★ a.	1120	…	…	…	…	…	…	…	1408	…	…	…	…	1811	…	…	…	…	…	…	2008	…	…	…
Paris Gare de Lyon d.	…	1218	…	…	1300	…	…	…	…	1550	…	1618	…	…	1933	2003	2009	…	2009	2009	…	…	2209	…
Dijon d.	…	1401	…	…	…	…	…	…	…	1732	…	…	…	…	2203	2236	2243	…	2243	2243	…	…	…	0046
Lyon Perrache d.	…	…	…	…	1507	…	…	…	…	…	…	…	…	…	…	…	…	…	…	…	…	…	…	…
Lyon Part Dieu d.	…	…	…	1501	1520	…	…	…	…	…	…	1826	1851	…	…	…	…	…	…	…	…	…	…	…
Chambéry d.	…	…	…	…	1640	…	…	…	…	…	…	2012	…	…	0035	…	0117	…	0117	0117	…	…	0359	…
Modane d.	…	…	…	…	1745	…	…	…	…	…	…	2117	…	…	…	…	…	…	…	…	…	…	0540	…
Vallorbe d.	…	1535	…	…	…	…	…	…	…	…	…	1909	…	…	…	…	…	…	…	…	…	…	…	…
Lausanne a.	…	1607	1613	…	…	…	…	…	…	…	1955	1945	…	…	…	…	…	…	…	…	…	…	…	…
Domodossola § a.	…	…	1811	…	…	…	…	…	…	…	2145	…	…	…	…	…	…	…	…	…	…	…	…	…
Stresa a.	…	…	…	…	…	…	…	…	…	…	…	…	…	…	…	…	…	…	…	…	…	…	…	…
Arona a.	…	…	1858	…	…	…	…	…	…	…	…	2217	…	…	…	…	…	…	…	…	…	…	…	…
Oulx a.	…	…	…	…	…	1811	…	…	…	…	…	2143	…	…	…	…	…	…	…	…	…	0706	…	…
Torino Porta Susa a.	…	…	…	…	…	…	…	…	…	…	…	2228	…	…	…	…	…	…	…	…	…	…	…	…
Torino Porta Nuova a.	…	…	…	…	…	1857	1910	1915	…	…	…	…	2316	…	…	…	…	…	…	…	…	0809	…	…
Novara a.	…	…	…	…	…	2016	…	…	…	…	…	…	2350	…	…	…	…	…	…	…	…	0845	…	…
Milano Centrale a.	…	…	1950	2005	…	…	…	2050	…	2350	2300	…	…	…	…	…	…	…	…	…	…	0845	…	1105
Genova Piazza Principe a.	…	…	…	…	…	2046	…	…	…	…	…	…	…	…	…	…	…	0604	0604	0645	…	…	…	…
Rapallo a.	…	…	…	…	…	2119	…	…	…	…	…	…	…	…	…	…	…	…	…	0715	…	…	…	…
La Spezia a.	…	…	…	…	…	2155	…	…	…	…	…	…	…	…	…	…	…	…	0711	0755	…	…	…	…
Viareggio a.	…	…	…	…	…	2234	…	…	…	…	…	…	…	…	…	…	…	…	…	0830	…	…	…	…
Pisa Centrale a.	…	…	…	…	…	2250	…	…	…	…	…	0656	…	…	…	…	…	…	0804	0845	…	…	…	…
Livorno a.	…	…	…	…	…	…	…	…	…	…	…	…	…	…	…	…	…	…	0823	0901	…	…	…	…
Grosseto a.	…	…	…	…	…	…	…	…	…	…	…	…	…	…	…	…	…	…	0938	1009	…	…	…	…
Verona a.	…	…	…	2130	…	…	…	…	…	…	…	…	…	…	0640	…	…	…	…	…	…	…	…	…
Padova a.	…	…	…	2221	…	…	…	…	…	…	…	…	…	…	0805	…	…	…	…	…	…	…	…	…
Venezia Mestre a.	…	…	…	2243	…	…	…	…	…	…	…	…	…	…	0833	…	…	…	…	…	…	…	…	…
Venezia Santa Lucia a.	…	…	…	2255	…	…	…	…	…	…	…	…	…	…	0845	…	…	…	…	…	…	…	…	…
Bologna Centrale a.	…	…	…	…	…	…	…	…	…	…	…	…	…	…	…	0810	0900	…	…	…	…	…	…	1256
Rimini a.	…	…	…	…	…	…	…	…	…	…	…	…	…	…	…	…	1003	…	…	…	…	…	…	1403
Ancona a.	…	…	…	…	…	…	…	…	…	…	…	…	…	…	…	…	1058	…	…	…	…	…	…	1455
Pescara Centrale a.	…	…	…	…	…	…	…	…	…	…	…	…	…	…	…	…	1223	…	…	…	…	…	…	1615
Bari Centrale a.	…	…	…	…	…	…	…	…	…	…	…	…	…	…	…	…	1517	…	…	…	…	…	…	1905
Brindisi Centrale a.	…	…	…	…	…	…	…	…	…	…	…	…	…	…	…	…	1632	…	…	…	…	…	…	2009
Patras 2770 a.	…	…	…	…	…	…	…	…	…	…	…	…	…	…	…	…	⊖	…	…	…	…	…	…	⊖
Athinai 2770 a.	…	…	…	…	…	…	…	…	…	…	…	…	…	…	…	…	⊖	…	…	…	…	…	…	⊖
Firenze SMN a.	…	…	…	…	…	2350	…	…	…	…	…	…	…	…	…	0938	…	…	…	…	…	…	…	…
Roma Termini a.	…	…	…	…	…	…	…	…	…	…	…	1005	…	…	…	…	…	…	1126z	…	1155	…	…	…
Napoli Centrale 370 a.	…	…	…	…	…	…	…	…	…	…	…	…	…	…	…	…	…	…	…	…	…	…	…	…

E – TRENO DELL'ETNA – Will **not** run Dec. 25, 31: 2 cl. and sleeper Torino - Siracusa (Table 400).
G – GALILEI – 1,2 cl., 1,2 cl. (T2) and 2 cl. Paris - Firenze.
L – PALATINO – 1,2 cl., 1,2 cl. (T2), 2 cl. and Paris - Roma.
R – RIALTO – 1,2 cl., 1,2 cl. (T2), 2 cl. and Paris - Venezia.
S – STENDHAL – 1,2 cl., 1,2 cl. (T2), 2 cl. and Paris - Milano.
V – Oct. 23 - Nov. 3, Dec. 20 - Jan. 6, Mar. 26 - May 31: 1,2 cl., 2 cl. and Paris - Roma Ostiense.
W – Sept. 29 - Oct. 22, Nov. 4 - Dec. 19, Jan. 7 - Mar. 25: and 2 cl. Paris - Genova.
c – Depart 13 minutes earlier on ⑦.
n – Depart 17 minutes earlier on ⑦.
r – Firenze Rifredi.
z – Roma Ostiense.

✓ – Supplement payable.
♣ – Special 'global' fares payable.
§ – Ticket point is Iselle.
◆ – Frontier/ticketing point.
☆ – Eurostar train. Special fares payable. Minimum check-in time 20 minutes. Timings are expected to change mid-May.
★ – Eurostar timings are 'emergency' timings valid to mid-May.
⊖ – For ship connections Brindisi - Patras (including bus Patras - Athinai) see Table 2770.
⊠ – For use by passengers making international journeys only.
CIS – CISALPINO Pendolino train.
FOR OTHER TRAIN NAMES SEE FOOT OF NEXT PAGE

Source: Thomas Cook.

•HYATT REGENCY ARUBA RESORT & CASINO

DELUXE   Map Dot ⑱

Juan Irausquin Boulevard #85
Phone: (297)8-61234   Fax: (297)8-65478
Affiliations: Hyatt Hotels & Resorts   HYATT   360 Rooms   Comm: R-10

Description/Location: Beachfront Resort (1990) reflecting Spanish-style architecture situated 4½ miles from Orangestad – Located 6 miles from Queen Beatrix International Airport

Accommodations: Air-conditioned rooms with private bath (hair dryer), remote-control color cable TV (movies, news), radio, direct-dial phone, minibar, safe & balcony; some with Jacuzzi, bathrobe, VCR and dual-line phone (bathroom extension) – 18 Suites – Executive Floor – Rooms for nonsmokers – Wheelchair Access – 24-hour Room Service

Dining/Entertainment: 4 Restaurants serving a variety of international cuisine, including one beachfront – Palms Bar – Pier Bar – Alfresco Bar and Lounge featuring nightly entertainment – Casino Bar with nightly entertainment – Copo Cabana Casino

Facilities/Services: 9 Meeting Rooms – 2 Ballrooms to 360 – Business Services Center – 2 Lighted Tennis Courts – Full Health Club – 3 level Outdoor Pool complex with cascade, waterslide and shallow area for kids – Games Room – Water Sports – Public Beach – Year-round Children's Supervised Activities Program – Concierge – Beauty Salon – Dry Cleaning – Babysitting – Car Rental – Gift Shop – Free Parking

Awards and Distinctions: AAA Four Diamonds 1991-2001 – Gold Key Award 2000 (Meetings & Conventions)

Rates: EP S/DWB ($220-360/365-535) Ste 1BR (495-1750/650-2150) 2BR (835-2035/1355-2610) EAP (45) – Max rates Dec 20-Apr 15 – Tax 17.66% – SC extra – Credit Cards: AE DC DIS MC VISA

RESERVATIONS:
Reps: HY – Toll-Free: (800)55-HYATT

•Holiday Inn Aruba
Beach Resort & Casino   600 Rooms   Map Dot ⑰

230 J.E. Irausquin Blvd., Palm Beach   PHONE: (297)8-63600   FAX: (297)8-65165

First Class Beachfront Resort Hotel (1969) set in well-lanscaped tropical grounds - Located 3 miles from downtown, 5 from airport - Air-conditioned rooms with private bath (hair dryer), direct-dial phone (dataport), coffeemaker, radio, remote-control color cable satellite TV (24-hour news channel, movies), safe, iron/ironing board & balcony with lounge chairs - 10 Suites - Rooms for nonsmokers - Wheelchair access - Room Service - 3 Restaurants - 3 Bars - Snack Bar - Lounge - Nightclub - Casino - Evening Entertainment - Meetings to 400 -Business Services - Outdoor Pool - 4 Tennis Courts - Exercise Room - Sauna - Jogging Track - Beach - Windsurfing School - Diving Center - Horseback Riding - Water Sports - Shops - Free Parking - Renovations in 1999
RATES: EP S/DWB ($105-175/209-269) EAP (15) - Max rates Apr 24-Dec 19 - SC 15% - Tax 17.6% - Ste rates avail - Energy surcharge rm/dly +(3) - MAP/AP avail   COMM: R-10   CREDIT CARDS: AE DC MC VISA   TD: 50%
RESERVATIONS: REPS: HOL Toll-Free: In US (800)HOLIDAY GDS: Sabre, Worldspan Internet: www.holidayinn-aruba.com

---

Source: Reprinted by permission of *Official Hotel Guide*, May 2001, pages 604 and 606 (partial).

A Cruise Itinerary

Sailing Dates

Day	Date	Port	Arrive	Depart
0	Jan 20	Los Angeles, CA		9:00 pm
1	Jan 21	Cruising the Pacific Ocean		
2	Jan 22	At Sea		
3	Jan 23	At Sea		
4	Jan 24	At Sea		
5	Jan 25	Kona, Hawaii	6:00 am	6:00 pm
6	Jan 26	Honolulu, Hawaii	8:00 am	midnight
7	Jan 27	Cruising the Pacific Ocean		
8	Jan 28	At Sea		
9	Jan 29	Crossing the Equator		
10	Jan 30	At Sea		
11	Jan 31	Crossing the International Dateline		
12	Feb2	Cruising the Pacific Ocean		
13	Feb3	At Sea		
14	Feb4	Port Vila, Vanuatu	8:00 am	5:00 pm
15	Feb 5	Cruising the Pacific Ocean		
16	Feb 6	Noumea, New Caledonia	7:00 am	4:00 pm
17	Feb 7	Cruising the Pacific Ocean		
18	Feb 8	BAY OF ISLANDS, NEW	1:00 pm	11:00 pm
19	Feb 9	Auckland, New Zealand	8:00 am	6:00 pm
20	Feb 10	Cruising the Pacific Ocean		
21	Feb 11	Lyttleton(Christchurch), New Zealand	7:00 am	6:30 pm
22	Feb 12	Port Chalmers(Dunedin), New Zealand	7:00 am	6:00 pm
23	Feb 13	Scenic Cruising		
23	Feb 13	Mifford Sound, New Zealand1	5:30 pm	6:00 pm
24	Feb 14	TASMEN SEA		
25	Feb 15	At Sea		
26	Feb 16	Sydney, Australia	6:00 am	
27	Feb 17	Sydney, Australia		6:30 pm
28	Feb 18	Cruising the Bass Strait		
29	Feb 19	Launceston, Tasmania	7:00 am	5:00 pm
29	Feb 19	Cruising Tamar River		
30	Feb 20	Melbourne, Australia	7:30 am	11:00pm
31	Feb 21	At Sea		
32	Feb 22	Adelaide, Australia	7:00 am	6:00 pm
33	Feb 23	At Sea		
34	Feb 24	Cruising the Indian Ocean		
35	Feb 25	Fremantle(Perth), Australia	7:00 am	9:00 pm
36	Feb 26	Cruising the Indian Ocean		
37	Feb 27	At Sea		
38	Feb 28	Broome, Australia	7:00 am	4:30 pm
39	Mar 1	Cruising the Timor Sea		
40	Mar 2	Darwin, Australia	6:00 am	8:00 pm
41	Mar 3	Cruising the Banda Sea		
42	Mar 4	Crossing the Equator		
43	Mar 5	Cruising the Philippine Sea		
44	Mar 6	Cebu, Philippines	8:00 am	5:00 pm
45	Mar 7	Cruising the South China Sea		
46	Mar 8	At Sea		
47	Mar 9	Hong Kong, China	7:00 am	
48	Mar 10	Hong Kong, China		
49	Mar 11	Hong Kong, China		5:00 pm
50	Mar 12	Cruising the South China Sea		
51	Mar 13	Da Nang, Vietnam	7:00 am	8:00 pm
52	Mar 14	Cruising the South China Sea		
53	Mar 15	At Sea		
54	Mar 16	Sihanoukville, Cambodia	6:00 am	10:00 pm
55	Mar 17	Cruising the South China Sea		
56	Mar 18	Singapore	7:00 am	7:00 pm
57	Mar 19	Port Kelang (Kuala Lumpur), Malaysia	6:30 am	4:30 pm
58	Mar 20	Phuket, Thailand	8:00 am	midnight
59	Mar 21	Cruising the Andaman Sea		
60	Mar 22	Cruising the Indian Ocean		
61	Mar 23	Madras, India	7:00 am	8:00 pm
62	Mar 24	Cruising the Gulf of Mannar		
63	Mar 25	Cruising the Indian Ocean		
64	Mar 26	At Sea		
65	Mar 27	Crossing the Equator		
66	Mar 28	Victoria, Seychelles	7:00 am	4:30 pm
67	Mar 29	Cruising the Indian Ocean		
68	Mar 30	Pt Louis, Mauritius	1:00 pm	11:00 pm
69	Mar 31	La Possession, Reunion	6:30 am	1:00 pm
70	Apr 1	Cruising the Indian Ocean		
71	Apr 2	At Sea		
72	Apr 3	Richards Bay, South Africa	8:00 am	11:00pm
73	Apr 4	Durban, South Africa	7:00 am	5:00 pm
74	Apr 5	Cruising the Indian Ocean		
75	Apr 6	Cape Town, South Africa	7:00 am	midnight
76	Apr 7	Cruising the Atlantic Ocean		
77	Apr 8	At Sea		
78	Apr 9	At Sea		
79	Apr 10	St Helena, United Kingdom	8:00 am	6:00 pm
80	Apr 11	Cruising the Atlantic Ocean		
81	Apr 12	At Sea		
82	Apr 13	At Sea		
83	Apr 14	At Sea		
84	Apr 15	Rio de Janeiro, Brazil	6:00 am	11:00pm
85	Apr 16	Cruising the Atlantic Ocean		
86	Apr 17	Salvador, Brazil	10:30 am	midnight
87	Apr 18	Cruising the Atlantic Ocean		
88	Apr 19	Recife, Brazil	7:00 am	5:00 pm
89	Apr 20	Cruising the Atlantic Ocean		
90	Apr 21	Crossing the Equator		
91	Apr 22	Devil's Island	11:00 am	6:00 pm
92	Apr 23	Cruising the Atlantic Ocean		
93	Apr 24	Roseau, Dominica	8:00 am	2:00 pm
93	Apr 24	Scenic cruising coast of Dominica		
93	Apr 24	Cabrits, Dominica1	4:00 pm	5:00 pm
94	Apr 25	St-Thomas, US V.I.	7:00 am	5:30 pm
95	Apr 26	Cruising the Atlantic Ocean		
96	Apr 27	At Sea		
97	Apr 28	Ft. Lauderdale, Florida	8:00 am	5:00 pm
98	Apr 29	Cruising the Atlantic Ocean		
99	Apr 30	New York, New York	9:00 am	

Click on a date to see pricing information for this sailing date.

Source: Reprinted by permission of Holland America.

Sensation Cruise Brochure

SENSATION
4 & 5 day cruise vacations from Tampa

Do you love the sensation of snorkeling through crystal-clear water, sailing across the sun-speckled sea and the primitive pleasure of feeling soft sand between your toes? Then you'll love a 4 or 5 day SENSATION vacation. The 4 day weekend getaway visits **Key West**, **Florida**, where every day is a "be yourself" festival. From there, Mexico! From **Playa del Carmen**, you can tour the fascinating Mayan ruins at Tulum. In sun-worshipping **Cozumel**, you can have fun in the sea, in every bargain-filled shop and just strolling along the city's beautiful avenidas.

The 5 day getaway also visits Cozumel/ Playa del Carmen, but your first exciting destination is **Grand Cayman**. While the capital city of George Town has museums, galleries and shops, you'll want to see all the out-of-town fun. This includes the gorgeous Seven Mile Beach and a heck of a town called Hell. Be sure to also visit Turtle Farm and Stingray City, where you swim with gentle stingrays that are soft as velvet. (Before or after your cruise, add a two or three night stay to explore the theme parks of Orlando and such famous Tampa attractions as Busch Gardens.)

When you have a craving for a specialty coffee or European pastry, slip into Joe's Café along Sensation Boulevard, the ship-long promenade.

Don't be fooled by the Roman décor of Michelangelo's lounge — it's a great place for a Manhattan, Singapore Sling or Irish Coffee.

Source: Reprinted by permission of Carnival Cruise Lines.

Sensation Cruise Brochure *(continued)*

4 Day Western Caribbean itinerary

DAY	PORT	ARRIVE	DEPART
Thurs.	Tampa		4:00 P.M.
Fri.	Key West	10:00 A.M.	3:30 P.M.
Sat.	Playa del Carmen*	Noon	12:30 P.M.
Sat.	Cozumel	1:30 P.M.	Midnight
Sun.	"Fun Day" at Sea		
Mon.	Tampa	8:00 A.M.	

*Operational stop for Tulum tour debarkation only.

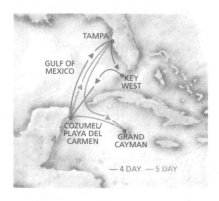

5 Day Western Caribbean itinerary

DAY	DAY	PORT	ARRIVE	DEPART
Mon.	Sat.	Tampa		4:00 P.M.
Tues.	Sun.	"Fun Day" at Sea		
Wed.	Mon.	Grand Cayman	7:00 A.M.	2:00 P.M.
Thurs.	Tues.	Playa del Carmen*	9:30 A.M.	10:00 A.M.
Thurs.	Tues.	Cozumel	11:00 A.M.	10:00 P.M.
Fri.	Wed.	"Fun Day" at Sea		
Sat.	Thurs.	Tampa	8:00 A.M.	

*Operational stop for Tulum tour debarkation only.

Combine SENSATION fun with sheer magic.
That's easy with one of Carnival's 7 Day Cruise &
Orlando Vacations. It includes an Orlando-area hotel
and rental car to let you see the many attractions of
Central Florida. For more information on these magical
land and sea combinations, refer to pages 30-31.

For departures through Saturday, August 10, 2002, the JUBILEE
will offer these itineraries. See pages 46-47 for the deck plan.

Leave your inhibitions aboard as you
trolley through laid-back Key West

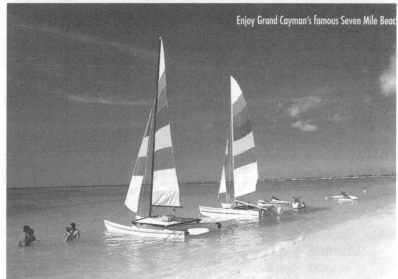

Enjoy Grand Cayman's famous Seven Mile Beach

Cozumel invites snorkelers from around the globe
with its crystal-clear turquoise water

32

Sensation Cruise Brochure *(continued)*

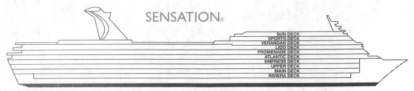

SENSATION®

SUN DECK
SPORTS DECK
VERANDAH DECK
LIDO DECK
PROMENADE DECK
ATLANTIC DECK
EMPRESS DECK
UPPER DECK
MAIN DECK
RIVIERA DECK

† Twin Bed/King and Double Convertible Sofa
†† Queen and Single Convertible Sofa
⁞ 2 Uppers
• 1 Upper
♦ Stateroom with 2 Porthole Windows

Staterooms are available that are modified for the physical challenged. Please call Carnival Reservations Department, Special Needs Desk, for details.

Gross Tonnage: 70,367   Length: 855 Feet   Beam: 103 Feet   Cruising Speed: 21 Knots
Guest Capacity: 2,052 (Double Occupancy)   Total Staff: 920   Registry: The Bahamas

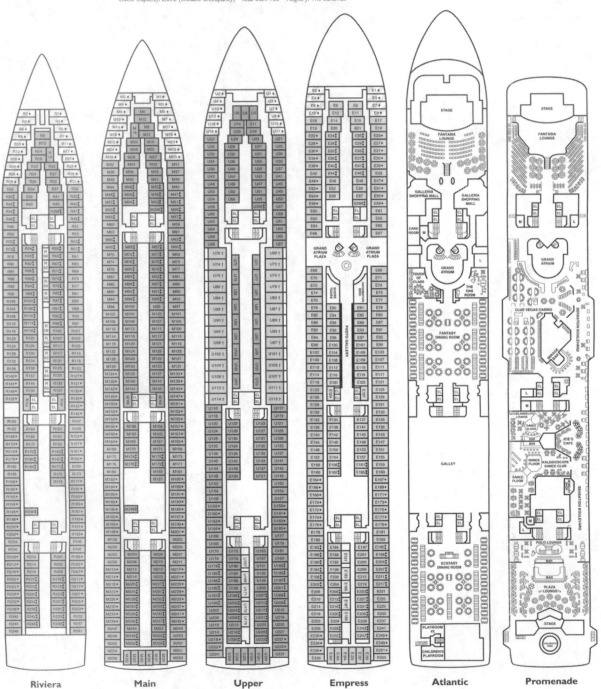

Riviera   Main   Upper   Empress   Atlantic   Promenade

34

Sensation Cruise Brochure *(continued)*

Carnival's **Fun** Plan **Finance**

4 Day from **$18***
per month

5 Day from **$19***
per month

*Based on Category 1A per guest, double-occupancy price. Fixed monthly payment is per guest, based on approval at the lowest APR and a 24-month payment term. Actual monthly payments and terms may vary depending on the applicant's credit qualifications.

Staterooms with partially obstructed views:
V23, V25, V27, V34, V38 & V42

SENSATION

You can't beat the value!

One low price includes virtually everything: accommodations, meals and snacks, 24-hour room service, fun activities, lavish entertainment, most shipboard activities, the Nautica Spa® gym and the supervised activities of the Camp Carnival® program.

Most Twin Beds Convert to King-Size Bed			4 Day		5 Day		7 Day Cruise & Orlando
Accommodation	Category	Deck	Brochure Rate	Super Saver Rate	Brochure Rate	Super Saver Rate	Super Saver Rate
SUITES WITH LARGE PRIVATE BALCONY	12	Upper	$1379	$899	$1749	$1149	$1299
	11	Verandah	1279	799	1549	949	1129
OCEAN VIEW	6D	Empress	1069	589	1269	669	869
	6C	Upper	1039	559	1229	629	829
	6B	Main	1009	529	1189	589	799
	6A	Riviera	979	499	1149	549	759
PORTHOLE	5A	Riviera, Main, Upper, Empress	929	449	1089	489	699
INTERIOR	4E	Verandah	959	479	1119	519	729
	4D	Empress	949	469	1109	509	719
	4C	Upper	939	459	1099	499	709
	4B	Main	929	449	1089	489	699
	4A	Riviera	899	419	1049	449	669
UPPER/LOWER	1A	Riviera, Upper, Empress	849	369	999	399	619

		4 Day		5 Day		7 Day
THIRD & FOURTH GUEST (SHARING STATEROOM WITH TWO ADULT GUESTS)		529	229	649	249	249
CRUISE VACATION PROTECTION PLAN	16 and under	29		39		59
	17 and over	49		59		99

For a 7 Day vacation that combines a 4 or 5 Day cruise with a 2 or 3 Night hotel stay, see pages 30-31 for our 7 Day Cruise & Orlando Vacations that offer the best of Central Florida. To create a 5 to 7 Day vacation package, add a 1 to 3 Day Tampa package (see pages 120-121) to the 4 or 5 Day cruise rates shown above. Single rates for the 7 Day Cruise and Orlando Vacations available upon request.

Super Saver Rates: The price of every "Fun Ship" cruise vacation varies based on departure date, category and date of booking. So, what's the best way to get significant savings on the "Fun Ship" vacation you choose? Easy. **Book early!**

2002 and 2003 DEPARTURE DATES

4 Day Cruises (Thursdays) | 5 Day Cruises (Mondays) | 5 Day Cruises (Saturdays)

2002 JUBILEE

Jan. 3, 17, 31	May 9, 23	Jan. 7, 21	May 13, 27	Jan. 12, 26	May 4, 18
Feb. 14, 28	June 6, 20	Feb. 4, 18	June 10, 24	Feb. 9, 23	June 1, 15, 29
March 14, 28	July 4, 18	March 4, 18	July 8, 22	March 9, 23	July 13, 27
April 11, 25	Aug. 1	April 1, 15, 29	Aug. 5	April 6, 20	Aug. 10

For departures through Saturday, August 10, 2002, **JUBILEE** will offer these itineraries. See pages 46-47 for the deck plan.

2002 SENSATION

Aug. 29	Nov. 7, 21	Sept. 2, 16, 30	Nov. 11, 25	Sept. 7, 21	Nov. 2, 16, 30
Sept. 12, 26	Dec. 5, 19	Oct. 14, 28	Dec. 9, 23*	Oct. 5, 19	Dec. 14, 28*
Oct. 10, 24					

2003 SENSATION

Jan. 2, 16, 30	July 3, 17, 31	Jan. 6, 20	July 7, 21	Jan. 11, 25	July 12, 26
Feb. 13, 27	August 14, 28	Feb. 3, 17	Aug. 4, 18	Feb. 8, 22	Aug. 9, 23
March 13, 27	Sept. 11, 25	March 3, 17, 31	Sept. 1, 15, 29	March 8, 22	Sept. 6, 20
April 10, 24	Oct. 9, 23	April 14, 28	Oct. 13, 27	April 5, 19	Oct. 4, 18
May 8, 22	Nov. 6, 20	May 12, 26	Nov. 10, 24	May 3, 17, 31	Nov. 1, 15, 29
June 5, 19	Dec. 4, 18	June 9, 23	Dec. 8, 22*	June 14, 28	Dec. 13, 27*

Air transportation available from major cities throughout North America. See pages 122-123 for details.

All rates quoted in U.S. dollars, per guest, double occupancy (except as noted).

Passenger Departure Tax, Customs Fee, Immigration Fee and other Governmental Taxes/Charges that vary by itinerary are additional per guest and range in total from $10 to $60.

*Holiday sailings: Monday, December 23, 2002; Saturday, December 28, 2002; Monday, December 22, 2003; and Saturday, December 27, 2003 rates may be slightly higher.

Special Single Guest Program: Guests requesting single occupancy of a stateroom may purchase the category requested from 150% to 200% of the double-occupancy rate (subject to availability).

BRIDGE

Sun

Lido

Verandah

Sports

Sensation Cruise Brochure *(continued)*

Things to know before you go.

Important Notice

Please be advised that federal law prohibits travel between two contiguous U.S. ports. Any guest who insists on departing in this situation accepts responsibility for any resulting penalties (e.g., you cannot board the ship in New Orleans and debark in Tampa).

Travel Hotline

For any last minute questions, just call our travel hotline at **1-877-TVL-HTLN** (1-877-885-4856) or 1-305-406-4779. Our representatives are on call to assist you with any question or travel emergency, 24 hours a day.

Embarkation

Embarkation begins as follows: Miami, Galveston and Tampa — 1:00 p.m.; Port Canaveral, New Orleans, and Los Angeles — 1:30 p.m.; San Juan — 2:30 p.m.; Vancouver — 12:30 p.m.; Seward (Egan Center in Anchorage) — 8:30 a.m. - 1:30 p.m. only; Honolulu — 1:00 p.m.; Ensenada — 6:00 p.m., complimentary motorcoach transportation is provided from the San Diego and Los Angeles airports, with embarkation aboard ship; San Diego (Panama Canal) departure — 1:30 p.m. **You must check in at least 30 minutes prior to departure.**

Debarkation

To allow sufficient time for Customs clearance, we recommend scheduling outbound air flights no earlier than 1:00 p.m., except for the following: Vancouver — Noon (Seattle departure — 2:00 p.m.); Anchorage — 12:45 p.m.; Honolulu — Noon; Ensenada — 2:00 p.m. for San Diego airport, 3:30 p.m. for Los Angeles airport.

Deposit and Payment

The following deposit is required in order to secure confirmed accommodations: 3, 4 and 5 Day Cruises — $100 per guest, balance payable no later than 60 days prior to departure date; 7 and 8 Day Cruises — $250 per guest, balance payable no later than 70 days prior to departure date; Alaska, CruiseTours and 10 day or longer cruises — $300 per guest, balance payable no later than 75 days prior to departure date. Carnival accepts American Express, VISA, MasterCard and Discover Card for all cruise payments.

Deposit, payment and cancellation terms may differ for groups; please consult any travel agent or Carnival for the terms that apply to your specific group.

Cancellation and Refunds

If a cancellation occurs, the following charges will be assessed:

	Days Prior to Departure Date	Cancellation Charge (per guest)
3, 4 & 5 day Cruises	Up to 61 days	None
	60 to 30 days	Deposit
	29 to 8 days	$150
	7 days or less	No Refund
7 and 8 day Cruises	Up to 71 days	None
	70 to 30 days	Deposit
	29 to 8 days	$350
	7 days or less	No Refund
Alaska Cruises, CruiseTours and 10 day or longer cruises	Up to 76 days	None
	75 to 46 days	Deposit
	45 to 15 days	50% of total fare
	14 days or less	No Refund

Name changes or additions will be allowed at Carnival's discretion and are subject to cancellation charges and rate increases.
Reservations will be held until 30 minutes prior to departure without risk of automatic cancellation. No refunds will be made in the event of "no shows" or interruption or cancellation by the guest after the start of the cruise. We recommend the purchase of trip cancellation insurance. See Carnival's Cruise Vacation Protection Plan on page 119.

Price Guarantee

Carnival reserves the right to increase published rates and air fare supplements without prior notice. However, fully paid or deposited guests will be protected, except for fuel surcharges, government taxes, other surcharges and changes to deposit, payment and cancellation terms/conditions, which are subject to change without notice. 2003 rates are slightly higher.

Change In Itinerary

When practicable, Carnival will promptly notify guests of a pre-cruise itinerary change through their travel agents or directly in the case of direct bookings. Carnival will offer such guests an opportunity to cancel their cruise without penalty within 24 hours. No additional compensation for the itinerary change will be offered at a later time. If an itinerary change occurs while a ship is at sea or when notice prior to sailing is not feasible, Carnival shall attempt to substitute an

alternative port. No compensation shall be provided to passengers when an alternative port is offered. If an alternative port is not provided, guests shall be provided a shipboard credit of $20 per person. The Vacation Guarantee shall not be affected by this policy.

The foregoing is a summary of the itinerary change policy and is qualified in its entirety by the complete policy which is posted on Carnival's web site at carnival.com.

Welcome Aboard

Our Welcome Aboard brochure will be sent along with your cruise documents. Please read it carefully, as it contains a wealth of information about your Carnival cruise.

Cruise Rates

Government taxes and fees, taxes on airline transportation, air transportation, shore excursions, medical services, items of a personal nature — such as bar beverages, gift shop purchases, beauty salon/barber shop and massage services, gambling and service/porterage gratuities — are not included in the cruise rate. The amount of the taxes and charges specified herein are subject to change. Carnival reserves the right to pass through to the guests any increases which become effective after the printing of this brochure.

Sail & Sign

For your convenience, charges for most of your onboard purchases are made to your Sail & Sign account. A required application form will be included with your documents. Carnival accepts American Express, VISA, MasterCard, Discover Card and cash for deposit on your account. (A minimum deposit will be required for cash accounts: 2 to 4 day Cruises, $100; 5 to 8 Day Cruises, $200; 9 Day or longer Cruises, $350.)

Service Charges

A $100 service charge will be assessed for issuing prepaid airline tickets. A $35 service charge will be assessed within 60 days of departure for the following: a) any cruise or vacation package changes (per guest, per change), except for stateroom upgrades or the addition of services; b) any change from Fly Aweigh to Cruise-Only status and changes of Fly Aweigh cities (per guest, per change); and c) research and/or providing copies of airline tickets or other documentation subsequent to your cruise (per request, payable in advance).

Liquor Policy

We are sorry, but guests are prohibited from bringing alcoholic beverages of any kind on board the ship for consumption. Alcoholic beverages purchased in the ship's gift shops or in foreign ports will be retained by Carnival until the end of the voyage. However, if you will be celebrating a special occasion while on board, fine wine or champagne may be brought on board during embarkation at the beginning of the cruise only. A $10 per bottle corkage fee will be charged should guests wish to consume this wine in the dining room. You may also purchase mixed drinks and other beverages from any of the ship's bars and lounges. **Alcoholic beverages will not be sold or served to anyone under the age of 21.** We reserve the right to refuse the sale of alcoholic beverages to anyone.

Tipping

How much you tip is a personal matter and completely up to you. However, we do have many guests who ask for guidelines in regard to what is appropriate. We suggest the following gratuities: Room Steward - $3.50 per guest, per day; Dining Room Team Service - $5.50 per guest, per day; Alternative Dining Service - $0.75 per guest, per day. Tipping your Maitre d' is at your discretion, based upon the service you received. Gratuities are customarily given the last evening of the cruise. Other service personnel, such as bar and room service staff, may be tipped as service is rendered. For your convenience on board the ship, a 15% gratuity is automatically included on all beverage tabs. Please note that you may prepay gratuities for all service personnel for a total of $9.75 per guest, per day. **For 2 Day Cruise-To-Nowhere, gratuities of $20 per guest must be prepaid.**

For your convenience, gratuities on certain ships are automatically added to your Sail & Sign card. Naturally, guests can adjust or remove gratuities at their discretion.

Clothing

Casual attire is in order during the day. For one or two nights, a dark suit or formal attire is suggested. The dress code for other evenings ranges from sport coat and tie to casual resort wear. Shorts and T-shirts are not permitted in the dining room during dinner. For Alaska cruises, sweaters, lightweight jackets and raincoats are suggested.

126

Sensation Cruise Brochure(*continued*)

Shore Tours

Optional shore tours are available for purchase aboard the ship. Please bring your completed order form (available on board) to the Information Desk. On select ships, you will be able to order directly through your in-stateroom Fun Vision® system. **These tours are operated by independent contractors and Carnival is not responsible for their actions.**

Dining Room Reservations

Dining preferences (time, companions) may be requested by your travel agent at the time of booking. By popular request, all our Dining Rooms are now Smoke-Free (smoking is permitted in designated areas and in your stateroom). **No requests are guaranteed.** Your table assignment will be confirmed at embarkation. Dining times are (subject to change):

	Main Seating	Late Seating
Breakfast (at sea)†	7:45 A.M.	9:00 A.M.
Lunch	NOON	1:30 P.M.
Dinner*	5:45 or 6:15 P.M.	8:00 or 8:30 P.M.

You can also enjoy a continental breakfast in your stateroom (until 10:00 a.m.) or a limited breakfast menu on deck. Lunch and dinner are also available bistro-style on the Lido Deck. (Seaview Bistro is not available on the last night of the cruise.) Spirit-class ships and CARNIVAL CONQUEST℠ have the added convenience of a reservations-only supper club (nominal fee will apply).

† Breakfast times vary by ship; these times are provided as a general guideline. Please check your daily Capers for exact times.

* We have four sittings for dinner on all ships except on Spirit-class ships (CARNIVAL SPIRIT℠, CARNIVAL PRIDE℠, CARNIVAL LEGEND℠), where we have two (Main-6:00 PM; Late-8:15 PM).

Special Diets

Special diet requirements may be requested by your travel agent at least two weeks prior to sailing. You should discuss the method of preparation of menu items with your waiter or headwaiter. There may be limitations in our ability to accommodate special orders. Kosher meals are not available.

Passport Data

U.S. Immigration determines the correct documents which guests must have in their possession in order to travel. **Proper travel documentation is required throughout the cruise and is the responsibility of the guest. Any guest traveling without proper documentation will not be allowed to board the vessel and no refund of cruise fare will be issued.** Documents must be presented at time of embarkation. All non-U.S. citizens must surrender their Passports and/or green cards and these documents will be returned at Immigration upon arrival back into the U.S. United States and Canadian guests need proof of citizenship (Passport, Birth Certificate or copy of Birth Certificate with raised seal) **and** photo I.D. Resident Aliens need **both** a Passport **and** an Alien Resident Card. Aliens need a valid Passport and a valid, unexpired U.S. Multiple Re-Entry Visa. Aliens eligible to apply for admission under the Visa Waiver Pilot Program must have a valid, unexpired Passport. Resident Aliens and Aliens must contact the appropriate consulate, U.S. Embassy or U.S. Immigration office to inquire about necessary travel documentation. In addition to the multiple-entry visa, Canada requires certain foreign nationals to obtain a Canadian visa. To debark for more than 24 hours in Mexico, guests must have obtained a Mexican Tourist Card from either a travel agent or a Mexican Consulate prior to their departure, and if debarking with children, must have a notarized affidavit from any absent parent indicating permission to travel with the accompanying adult.

Minor Guests

Guests under the age of 21 years must be accompanied by a parent, grandparent or guardian 25 years or older in the same stateroom. Infants must be at least four months old to be eligible to travel. Guests under the age of 21 staying at any hotel in conjunction with Carnival's Fly Aweigh® program or vacation packages may be required to be accompanied by a guest 21 years or older in the same room as per each hotel's policy. Permission for minor guests to fly unaccompanied is permitted/denied by the airlines as per each airline's rules. Guests should check with their scheduled airline for eligibility. Carnival assumes no responsibility for guests under 21 years traveling unaccompanied by air. **Our Camp Carnival® program features supervised activities for children 2-15, with limited activities available for 16- to 18-year-olds.**

Please note that guests under 16 are not permitted in the Casino and Nautica Spa®. Guests between the ages of 16 and 18 must be accompanied by an adult at all times in these facilities.

Visitors

Carnival has a no visitors policy and regrets any inconvenience this may cause.

Medical Services

Should you require medical attention while onboard, our infirmary staff are available to assist you 24 hours a day. Our shipboard infirmaries meet or exceed the Medical Facilities Guidelines established by the International Council of Cruise Lines and the American College of Emergency Physicians. The medical staff is from the fields of Emergency medicine and/or Family practice, and is certified in Advanced Cardiac Life Support.

Our physicians are independent contractors and as such, are entitled to render services at a customary charge. The charge for their services and any other medical expenses will be applied to your Sail & Sign account.

Pregnancy: Please be advised that guests who are 27 weeks or more into their pregnancy at the time of the voyage will not be permitted to sail because of the risk of premature labor.

Guests with Special Needs

Carnival seeks, to the extent feasible, to accommodate guests with special needs so they are able to enjoy our ships and other facilities. For example, service animals are permitted onboard ships if prior arrangements have been made at time of booking. In situations where a guest with special needs, such as a guest in a wheelchair, would be unable to be comfortably accommodated due to vessel safety barriers and other criteria, we may find it necessary to ask the guest to bring along a companion to assist, or to make alternative arrangements. Guests who have any medical, physical or other special needs are required to contact our Special Needs Desk at 1-800-438-6744, ext. 70025 or TTY (for hearing impaired) at 1-800-972-4386 to discuss the details of their specific special needs.

Baggage Liability

We highly recommend that all guests purchase a vacation protection policy covering baggage, contents and accidents. Carnival's Cruise Vacation Protection Plan℠ is a comprehensive program that is attractively priced. If you choose not to purchase insurance, Carnival's liability for lost or damaged baggage, contents and personal possessions is limited to a maximum of $50 per bag with a maximum total limitation of $100 per stateroom regardless of the number of bags. Carnival cannot accept liability for loss or theft of money, jewelry or other valuables left in the stateroom or public areas on board. Safe-deposit boxes are available in your stateroom, as well as at the Information Desk at no charge ($25 refundable key deposit). We highly recommend guests personally carry any valuables, medication or breakable items on and off the ship.

Baggage Assistance

Curbside porters are available at the pier during embarkation to take luggage to the vessel for delivery to your stateroom. Please be sure each piece of luggage is locked and has a tag listing your name, ship and stateroom number. Customary tip is $1 per bag. Curbside porters are not employees of Carnival; therefore, any problems are the responsibility of the guest. Carnival assumes no responsibility for carry-on luggage. Any luggage left at the pier will be forwarded at the guest's expense. Claims for luggage loss or damage must be made in writing to the debarkation personnel prior to leaving the pier area.

Advanced or Delayed Sailings

In the event of strikes, lockouts, riots and stoppage of labor from whatever cause, or for any other reason whatsoever, including inclement weather, the ship owner may at any time cancel, advance or postpone any scheduled sailing and may, but is not obliged to, substitute another vessel and shall not be liable for any loss to guests by reason of such cancellation or substitution.

Reservations are subject to change in the event of a full-ship charter.

Responsibility

Carnival neither controls, nor operates, nor is responsible for the actions of independent contractors, such as airlines, railroad companies, tour operators or ground transporters. Carnival denies any responsibility or liability for late arrival of your flight or train or for any illness, injury, damage, loss of cruise time or other irregularities resulting therefrom. Carnival's responsibility does not extend beyond the vessel.

You are responsible for arriving at the respective ports on time for embarkation and for joining the vessel at its next port of call if, for any reason, you miss a scheduled sailing. Carnival reserves the right to refuse or discontinue passage to anyone when, in Carnival's judgement, it would be considered a risk to the guest's own safety and well-being or the health, safety, well-being, comfort and enjoyment of any other guest or crew member.

Cruise passage is subject to the terms and conditions shown on Carnival Cruise Lines' "Terms and Conditions of Passage Contract Ticket" (copies available upon request), including the procedure for the resolution of disputes which must take place in Miami-Dade County, Florida.

For travel agent use only: Carnival Reservations (800) 327-9501.

All prices are quoted in U.S. dollars.

127

CLIA *Cruise Manual*

48

Name	Sensation
Company	Carnival Cruise Lines
Originally Built	1993
Country of Registry	The Bahamas
Speed	21 knots
Normal Crew Size	920
Nationality of Crew	
Officers	Italian
Hotel Staff	International
Cruise Staff	International

SIZE/CAPACITY

Tonnage	70,367
Length	855 feet
Beam	103 feet
Total Capacity (incl. uppers)	2,606
Normal Cruise Cap. (basis 2)	2,052
Space Ratio	34.1

ACCOMMODATIONS

Type	No. Outside	No. Inside
Suites *†	28	
Demi Suites *	26	
Twins *	564	389
Uppers/ Lowers		19
Total	618	408
Total Cabins	1,026	

* All convert to king size beds.
† Include bathtub whirlpools.

OTHER USEFUL INFORMATION

No. of dinner sittings 2
Usual dinner hours 6:00pm & 8:00pm
Dining room dress code
  Casual, no shorts at night
  2 formal nights on 7-day cruises
Special diet meals
  Diabetic, low salt, vegetarian, bland
Tipping Policy
  Cabin Steward, $3.50 per person per day*
  Waiter, $3.50 per person per day*
  Asst. Waiter, $2.00 per person per day*
  15% on bar tabs payable at time
  of purchase

Payable at end of cruise

PUBLIC ROOM CAPACITIES

A Touch of Class	92
The Oak Room	43
Fantasy Dining Room	650
Ecstasy Dining Room	658
Fantasia Lounge	1,300+
Sensation Boulevard	230
Club Vegas Casino	450
Joe's Cafe	58
Michelangelo Lounge	109
Kaleidoscope Dance Club	230+
Plaza Lounge	541
Polo Lounge	92
Seaview Bar & Grill	722

FACILITIES

Barber Shop
Bar & Lounges (10)
Beauty Salon
Bow Thrusters (3)
Child Counselors
Children's Playrooms (2)
Closed Circuit TV
Diesel Electronic Propulsion System
Dining Rooms (2)
Drug Store
Duty Free Shops & Galleria Shopping Mall
Elevators (14)
Engines (6) developing approx. 56,000 HP
Fully Air Conditioned
Full Casino
Fully Equipped Nautica/Spa & Health Club
Infirmary
Jogging Track (1/8 mile)
Photo Gallery
Pizzeria
Satellite TV at sea
Shore Excursion Office
Shuffleboard
Stabilizers
Stern Thrusters
Swimming Pools Outside (3)
Twin Rudders individually controlled
VCR Rentals

Source: Reprinted by permission of CLIA, *2001 Cruise Manual.*

Norway Tour Brochure

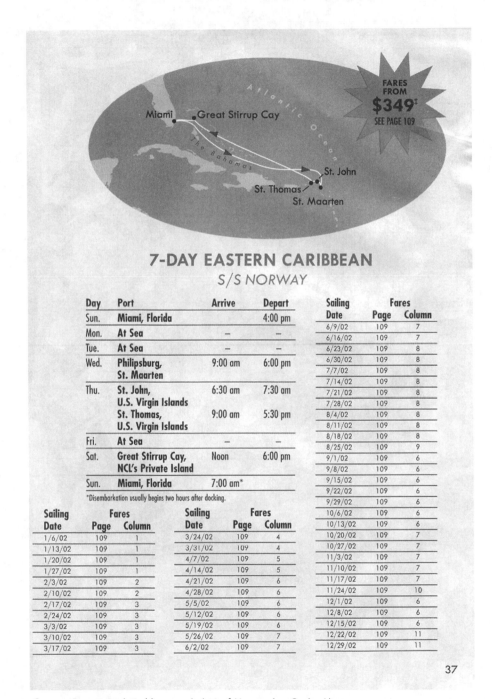

FARES FROM $349‡ SEE PAGE 109

7-DAY EASTERN CARIBBEAN
S/S NORWAY

Day	Port	Arrive	Depart
Sun.	**Miami, Florida**		4:00 pm
Mon.	**At Sea**	—	—
Tue.	**At Sea**	—	—
Wed.	**Philipsburg, St. Maarten**	9:00 am	6:00 pm
Thu.	**St. John, U.S. Virgin Islands**	6:30 am	7:30 am
	St. Thomas, U.S. Virgin Islands	9:00 am	5:30 pm
Fri.	**At Sea**	—	—
Sat.	**Great Stirrup Cay, NCL's Private Island**	Noon	6:00 pm
Sun.	**Miami, Florida**	7:00 am*	

*Disembarkation usually begins two hours after docking.

Sailing Date	Fares Page	Column
1/6/02	109	1
1/13/02	109	1
1/20/02	109	1
1/27/02	109	1
2/3/02	109	2
2/10/02	109	2
2/17/02	109	3
2/24/02	109	3
3/3/02	109	3
3/10/02	109	3
3/17/02	109	3

Sailing Date	Fares Page	Column
3/24/02	109	4
3/31/02	109	4
4/7/02	109	5
4/14/02	109	5
4/21/02	109	6
4/28/02	109	6
5/5/02	109	6
5/12/02	109	6
5/19/02	109	6
5/26/02	109	7
6/2/02	109	7

Sailing Date	Fares Page	Column
6/9/02	109	7
6/16/02	109	7
6/23/02	109	8
6/30/02	109	8
7/7/02	109	8
7/14/02	109	8
7/21/02	109	8
7/28/02	109	8
8/4/02	109	8
8/11/02	109	8
8/18/02	109	8
8/25/02	109	9
9/1/02	109	6
9/8/02	109	6
9/15/02	109	6
9/22/02	109	6
9/29/02	109	6
10/6/02	109	6
10/13/02	109	6
10/20/02	109	7
10/27/02	109	7
11/3/02	109	7
11/10/02	109	7
11/17/02	109	7
11/24/02	109	10
12/1/02	109	6
12/8/02	109	6
12/15/02	109	6
12/22/02	109	11
12/29/02	109	11

37

Source: Pages reprinted by permission of Norwegian Cruise Line.

Norway Tour Brochure (continued)

7-DAY EASTERN CARIBBEAN

COLUMN NUMBER	BROCHURE RATE	1	2	3	4	5	6	7	8	9	10	11
BOOK EARLY & SAVE UP TO:		50%	50%	45%	40%	45%	35%	30%	20%	30%	25%	15%
SAILING DATES		1/6/02 1/13/02 1/20/02 1/27/02	2/3/02 2/10/02	2/17/02 2/24/02 3/3/02 3/10/02 3/17/02	3/24/02 3/31/02	4/7/02 4/14/02	4/21/02 4/28/02 5/5/02 5/12/02 5/19/02 9/1/02 9/8/02 9/15/02 9/22/02 9/29/02 10/6/02 10/13/02 12/1/02 12/8/02 12/15/02	5/26/02 6/2/02 6/9/02 6/16/02 10/20/02 10/27/02 11/3/02 11/10/02 11/17/02	6/23/02 6/30/02 7/7/02 7/14/02 7/21/02 7/28/02 8/4/02 8/11/02 8/18/02	8/25/02	11/24/02	12/22/02 12/29/02
STATEROOM CATEGORIES		EBF	EBF	EBF	EBF	EBF	EBF	EBF	EBF	EBF	EBF	EBF
AA Owner's Suite	$3,499	$2,149	$2,149	$2,199	$2,249	$2,199	$2,299	$2,349	$2,449	$2,349	$2,399	$2,499
AB Penthouse	2,649	1,649	1,649	1,699	1,749	1,699	1,799	1,849	1,949	1,849	1,899	1,999
AC Penthouse	1,679	1,149	1,149	1,199	1,249	1,199	1,299	1,349	1,449	1,349	1,399	1,499
AD Penthouse	1,569	1,049	1,049	1,099	1,149	1,099	1,199	1,249	1,349	1,249	1,299	1,399
AE Suite	1,459	949	949	999	1,049	999	1,099	1,149	1,249	1,149	1,199	1,299
AF Suite	1,349	849	849	899	949	899	999	1,049	1,149	1,049	1,099	1,199
AG Suite	1,269	N/A	N/A	N/A	N/A	N/A	N/A	N/A	N/A	N/A	N/A	N/A
CC Oceanview Stateroom	1,159	669	669	719	769	719	819	869	969	869	919	1,019
C Oceanview Stateroom	1,149	649	649	699	749	699	799	849	949	849	899	999
DD Oceanview Stateroom	1,099	629	629	679	729	679	779	829	929	829	879	979
D Oceanview Stateroom	1,079	609	609	659	709	659	759	809	909	809	859	959
E Oceanview Stateroom	1,059	589	589	639	689	639	739	789	889	789	839	939
F Oceanview Stateroom	1,029	569	569	619	669	619	719	769	869	769	819	919
G Oceanview Stateroom	1,009	549	549	599	649	599	699	749	849	749	799	899
HH Oceanview Stateroom	979	N/A	N/A	N/A	N/A	N/A	N/A	N/A	N/A	N/A	N/A	N/A
H Oceanview Stateroom	959	N/A	N/A	N/A	N/A	N/A	N/A	N/A	N/A	N/A	N/A	N/A
II Inside Stateroom	949	479	479	529	579	529	629	679	779	679	729	829
I Inside Stateroom	909	459	459	509	559	509	609	659	759	659	709	809
JJ Inside Stateroom	899	439	439	489	539	489	589	639	739	639	689	789
J Inside Stateroom	889	419	419	469	519	469	569	619	719	619	669	769
K Inside Stateroom	879	399	399	449	499	449	549	599	699	599	649	749
L Inside Stateroom	869	N/A	N/A	N/A	N/A	N/A	N/A	N/A	N/A	N/A	N/A	N/A
M Inside Stateroom	859	N/A	N/A	N/A	N/A	N/A	N/A	N/A	N/A	N/A	N/A	N/A
N Inside Stateroom	849	N/A	N/A	N/A	N/A	N/A	N/A	N/A	N/A	N/A	N/A	N/A
O Oceanview Stateroom	829	399	399	449	499	449	549	599	699	599	649	749
P Inside Stateroom	799	349	349	399	449	399	499	549	549	549	599	699
3rd/4th Guests+	449	199	299	299	299	199	199	299	299	299	199	399

S/S NORWAY'S AMENITIES

4 Restaurants
• Windward Restaurant
• Leeward Restaurant
• The Great Outdoor Restaurant
• Le Bistro French Restaurant

8 Bars and Lounges
• Sports Bar
• Club Internationale
• Dazzles
• North Cape Lounge
• Windjammer Bar
• Topsiders Bar
• Pool Bar
• Casino Bar

Other Amenities
• 2 Swimming Pools
• 2 Hot Tubs
• Roman Spa
• 24-Hour Fitness Center
• Jogging/Walking Track
• Basketball/Volleyball Court
• Monte Carlo Casino
• Shops
• Library/Card Room
• The Porthole Playroom
• Trolland
• Saga Theatre
• Internet Café
• Svenn's Ice Cream Parlor
• Conference Center

BOOK EARLY & SAVE!
Enjoy great savings when you book in advance.

All prices quoted in U.S. dollars and are cruise only, per person based on double occupancy. Government taxes and fees of $30 to $43 are not included. Group and charter rates available on request. Guaranteed singles accommodation pricing is available. See your travel professional for details. Standard Single Occupancy Fare: Guests requesting single occupancy of a stateroom within a specific fare category will be charged 150-200% of the fare for the selected accommodation. Fares subject to availability.

+ Per person, two years and older, who share accommodations with two full-fare paying adults.

109

S/S Norway *Deck Plans*

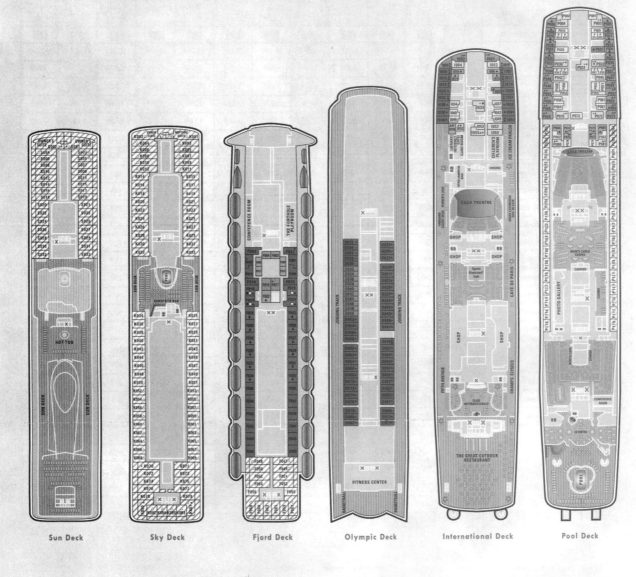

Sun Deck   Sky Deck   Fjord Deck   Olympic Deck   International Deck   Pool Deck

SKY DECK
OLYMPIC DECK
POOL DECK
NORWAY DECK
BISCAYNE DECK
DOLPHIN DECK

SUN DECK

STAR DECK

FJORD DECK

INTERNATIONAL DECK
VIKING DECK
ATLANTIC DECK
CARIBBEAN DECK

Gross Tonnage: 76,049. Overall Length: 1,035 feet. Beam: 110 feet.
Draft: 35.5 feet. Engines: Parsons Turbines—4 boilers. Cruise Speed: 25 knots.
Guests: 2,032 (double occupancy). Crew: 1,000.

All staterooms on *S/S Norway* have a TV, duvet
and bathroom with bathtub and/or shower.

For more information, contact NCL Reservations.

Norway Tour Brochure *(continued)*

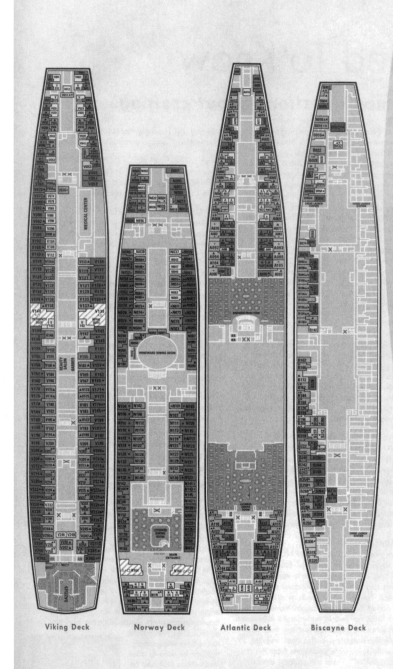

Viking Deck **Norway Deck** **Atlantic Deck** **Biscayne Deck**

S/S NORWAY CATEGORIES

AA **OWNER'S SUITE** *Sun, Sky, Viking Decks* Living room, private wraparound balcony (Sun Deck only). Floor-to-ceiling windows (Sun and Sky Decks only). Bedroom with king-size bed, refrigerator, tub and shower, vanity, Roman tub & hot tub (Sun and Sky Decks only). Concierge available.

AB **PENTHOUSE** *Sky, Fjord Decks* Sitting area, private balcony, king-size bed, floor-to-ceiling windows, refrigerator, tub and shower, vanity. Concierge available.

AC **PENTHOUSE** *Sun, Sky, Fjord Decks* Sitting area, private balcony, two lower beds or king-size bed, floor-to-ceiling windows, refrigerator, tub and shower, vanity. Concierge available. (Some Fjord Deck staterooms have obstructed views.)

AD **PENTHOUSE** *Sun, Sky Decks* Sitting area, private balcony, two lower beds or king-size bed, floor-to-ceiling windows, refrigerator, tub and shower. Concierge available.

AE **SUITE** *Sky, Fjord, Norway Decks* Sitting area, two lower beds or king-size bed, floor-to-ceiling windows (except Norway Deck), refrigerator, tub and shower, vanity. Concierge available. (Fjord Deck staterooms have obstructed views.)

AF **SUITE** *Sky, Fjord, Pool Decks* Sitting area, two lower beds or queen- or king-size bed, floor-to-ceiling windows (Sky or Fjord Decks only), large picture windows (Pool Deck only), refrigerator, tub and shower, vanity. Concierge available.

AG **SUITE** *Pool Deck* Sitting area, two lower beds, large picture windows, refrigerator, tub and shower, vanity. Concierge available.

CC **OCEANVIEW STATEROOM** *Viking, Norway Decks* Two lower beds, porthole, refrigerator.

C **OCEANVIEW STATEROOM** *Fjord, Norway Decks* Queen or double bed, picture window or porthole, refrigerator. (Fjord Deck staterooms have obstructed views.)

DD **OCEANVIEW STATEROOM** *Fjord, Olympic, International, Viking, Norway Decks* Two lower beds, picture window or porthole, refrigerator. (Fjord Deck staterooms have obstructed views.)

D **OCEANVIEW STATEROOM** *Olympic, Pool, Viking, Norway Decks* Double bed, picture window or porthole.

E **OCEANVIEW STATEROOM** *International, Pool, Viking, Norway Decks* Two lower beds, picture window or porthole.

F **OCEANVIEW STATEROOM** *Atlantic, Biscayne Decks* Double bed, porthole.

G **OCEANVIEW STATEROOM** *Atlantic, Biscayne Decks* Two lower beds, porthole.

HH **OCEANVIEW STATEROOM** *Biscayne Deck* Two lower beds, porthole.

H **OCEANVIEW STATEROOM** *Biscayne Deck* Two lower beds, porthole.

II **INSIDE STATEROOM** *Fjord, Viking, Norway Decks* Two lower beds.

I **INSIDE STATEROOM** *Fjord, International, Pool, Viking, Norway Decks* Double bed.

JJ **INSIDE STATEROOM** *International, Pool, Viking, Norway Decks* Two lower beds.

J **INSIDE STATEROOM** *International, Pool, Atlantic, Biscayne Decks* Double bed.

K **INSIDE STATEROOM** *Atlantic, Biscayne Decks* Two lower beds.

L **INSIDE STATEROOM** *Biscayne Deck* Two lower beds.

M **INSIDE STATEROOM** *Biscayne Deck* Two lower beds.

N **INSIDE STATEROOM** *Biscayne Deck* Two lower beds.

O **OCEANVIEW STATEROOM** *Viking, Norway, Atlantic, Biscayne Decks* Upper and lower beds.

P **INSIDE STATEROOM** *International, Pool, Viking, Norway, Atlantic, Biscayne Decks* Upper and lower beds.

111

Cosmos Tour Brochure

COSMOS — *WORLD'S BEST BUDGET TOURING* — **ESCORTED**

Alpine Adventure

Featuring the Bernina Express Train

Tour **6060** — 14 days incl.air, or 13 days Frankfurt/Frankfurt
Tour **5660/5661** — including OBERAMMERGAU PASSION PLAY

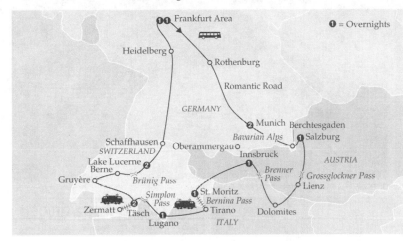

ALL THIS IS INCLUDED

- Scheduled transatlantic flights and airport transfers in Frankfurt if Cosmos issues the tickets; see page 13

- Services of a professional tour director

- Hotels listed below or equivalent; see also page 9. Rooms with private bath or shower, hotel taxes, porterage, tips, and service charges

- 12 continental breakfasts (B); 7 dinners (D)

- Touring by private first-class air-conditioned motorcoach

- The Bernina Express Train; Mountain Train Täsch-Zermatt

- Visits to Frankfurt, Rothenburg, Munich (tour 6060 only), Linderhof Castle* (tour 6060 only) and Oberammergau, Berchtesgaden, Salzburg, Lienz, Innsbruck, St. Moritz, Lugano, Täsch, Zermatt, Gruyère village, Berne, Interlaken, Lucerne, Heidelberg (*entrance fee included)

- Scenic highlights: Romantic Road, Bavarian Alps, Alpine Dolomites, Tyrolean Alps, Engadine Valley, Swiss-Italian Lake District, Bernese Oberland, Rhine Falls, Rhine Valley

- Alpine passes: Grossglockner, Brenner, Simplon, Brünig

- Portfolio of travel documents

Day 1, Fri. BOARD YOUR OVERNIGHT TRANSATLANTIC FLIGHT.

Day 2, Sat. ARRIVAL IN FRANKFURT AREA, GERMANY. Check into your hotel. The rest of the day is free. Tonight meet your tour director and fellow travelers.

Day 3, Sun. FRANKFURT AREA-ROMANTIC ROAD-MUNICH. The highlight today is undoubtedly the Romantic Road, which runs north to south as far as the Alps. See Rothenburg with its ramparts and towers, cobbled streets, and 16th-century houses. Next to lovely medieval Nördlingen. By evening journey towards the Danube Valley to Munich. (B,D)

Day 4, Mon. MUNICH. EXCURSION TO THE BAVARIAN ALPS AND CASTLES. Your orientation drive of Germany's "secret capital" includes the 1,000-foot-high Television Tower and Marienplatz with the Old and New Town Hall and the celebrated carillon clock. In the afternoon an included excursion into the heart of the Bavarian Alps: stop at Ettal Abbey for pictures and maybe a sip of the famous Klosterlikör; tour charming Linderhof Castle, once the hunting retreat of Bavarian royalty; finally visit Oberammergau, the Passion Play village. Then back to Munich. (B)

Day 5, Tue. MUNICH-SALZBURG, AUSTRIA. A memorable day full of grand scenery culminates in a visit to Berchtesgaden near Lake Königsee. Picturesquely situated in its own valley, it is surrounded by mountain peaks, one of which is known as the "Eagle's Nest." From here only a few more miles and you're in Salzburg. (B,D)

Day 6, Wed. SALZBURG-INNSBRUCK. Scenic splendor in the heart of the Austrian Alps: enjoy superb views of glaciers and mountain peaks as your driver carefully negotiates the 26 hairpin bends of the Grossglockner Pass to Lienz. Cross into Italy for an entirely different, but equally magnificent type of scenery, the Dolomites. From here you take the Brenner Pass highway to Innsbruck, capital of the Austrian Tyrol. This evening there's an optional folklore show. (B,D)

▼ *AUSTRIAN TRADITIONAL DRESS*

▼ *THE RHINE FALLS AT SCHAFFHAUSEN*

Source: Pages reprinted by permission of Globus & Cosmos Tours.

Cosmos Tour Brochure *(continued)*

▲ *THE GORNERGRAT RAILWAY — BENEATH THE MATTERHORN, ZERMATT*

▲ *MUNICH'S TOWN HALL*

Day 7, Thu. INNSBRUCK-ST. MORITZ, SWITZERLAND. An orientation tour in Innsbruck includes the famous Golden Roof. Later drive through wonderful mountain scenery into Switzerland. Spend the night in St. Moritz, an international resort for over 100 years and home of the famous Cresta Run. Set in the Engadine Valley on the shores of a blue lake, equally attractive for winter and summer vacations. (B)

Day 8, Fri. ST. MORITZ-THE BERNINA EXPRESS TRAIN TO TIRANO, ITALY-LUGANO, SWITZERLAND. Enjoy the highlight of the whole tour and a wonderful way of crossing the Alps. One of Europe's most spectacular train rides begins in St. Moritz and takes you across the lofty Bernina Pass via the Swiss Poschiavo area to Tirano in the Italian Valtellina. Here rejoin your coach for the journey to the shores of Lake Lugano. (B,D)

Day 9, Sat. LUGANO-LAKE MAGGIORE-SIMPLON PASS-TÄSCH. Morning in Lugano, an elegant resort in the Italian-speaking part of Switzerland. Afterwards return to Italy to savor the luminous atmosphere of Lake Maggiore, set in almost Mediterranean scenery. There is an optional boat trip to the island of Isola Bella. Then back into Switzerland via the scenic Simplon Pass. Overnight in the village of Täsch. (B,D)

Day 10, Sun. TÄSCH-ZERMATT EXCURSION. Almost a whole day to enjoy one of Switzerland's best-known winter and summer resorts. Reach it by the short alpine train journey. There's a variety of shops, cafés, and bars, and the narrow streets are traffic-free. Later enjoy the optional ride on Europe's highest rack-railway to 10,272-foot Gornergrat for breathtaking views of the Alps. Return to Täsch for overnight. (B,D)

Day 11, Mon. TÄSCH-BERNE-LAKE LUCERNE. More glorious alpine scenery as you journey towards the heart of Switzerland. Stop awhile in Gruyère, once a medieval stronghold standing safe within its ramparts on a high crag. On to Switzerland's beautiful capital, Berne, a charming town with arcaded shops, carved fountains, and towers. Then by way of the shores of Lake Thun to Interlaken, gateway to the Bernese Oberland. Situated between two lakes and in the shadow of towering mountains, this is a year-round resort with many tourist attractions. Later on into Lucerne itself for an optional folklore evening. (B)

Day 12, Tue. LUCERNE. One of Switzerland's finest cities nestled amid its snow-capped alps, surrounded by its lake, and embellished by the clear mountain waters of the River Reuss. Your sightseeing takes in the impressive city walls, a covered wooden bridge, ornate patrician houses lining cobblestone streets, and the Lion Monument — a masterful stone sculpture in honor of the heroic Swiss Guard of Louis XVI. A grand selection of optional activities completes the day: a cable car ride to the 10,000-foot summit of the Mount Titlis, a cruise on the fjord-like lake, and of course there is time to shop for that very Swiss watch. (B,D)

Day 13, Wed. LAKE LUCERNE-RHINE FALLS-FRANKFURT AREA, GERMANY. Start the day with a stop to see the mighty Rhine Falls as they cascade towards their final destination, the North Sea. More exciting sights today. Last glimpses of the Black Forest and then sweeping views of the Rhine Valley; finally Heidelberg, Germany's oldest university town of Student Prince fame. Stop awhile here to enjoy the bustle of this lively city. Then back to Frankfurt area for overnight. (B)

Day 14, Thu. YOUR HOMEBOUND FLIGHT ARRIVES THE SAME DAY. (B)

➤ *If you need a visa for Italy, please secure a multiple-entry visa.*

TOUR 5660/5661 - 14 DAYS
OBERAMMERGAU PASSION PLAY

Days 1 to 2 Like tour 6060.

Day 3 FRANKFURT-OBERAMMERGAU. Through the Romantic Road to Oberammergau, the Passion Play village in the Bavarian Alps. (B,D)

Day 4 OBERAMMERGAU. All day devoted to the Passion Play. See page 6 for details. (B,L,D)

Day 5 OBERAMMERGAU-SALZBURG, AUSTRIA. Continue into Austria to Salzburg. (B,D)

Days 6 to 14 Like tour 6060.

Tours 6060 and 5660/5661
DATES & PRICES

Departure number	Leave USA or join Frankfurt next day	Tour 6060		Tour 5660/1	
		14 days USA/USA* US$	13 days Frankfurt/Frankfurt US$	14 days USA/USA* US$	13 days Frankfurt/Frankfurt US$
0415	Fri 14 Apr	1600	898	—	—
0422	Fri 21 Apr	1600	898	—	—
0429	Fri 28 Apr	1600	898	—	—
0506	Fri 05 May	1630	928	—	—
0513	Fri 12 May	1630	928	—	—
0520	Fri 19 May	1630	928	2001	1299
0527	Fri 26 May	1650	948	2001	1299
0603	Fri 02 Jun	1789	948	2140	1299
0610	Fri 09 Jun	1789	948	2140	1299
0617	Fri 16 Jun	1789	948	2140	1299
0624	Fri 23 Jun	1789	948	2140	1299
0701	Fri 30 Jun	1799	958	2140	1299
0708	Fri 07 Jul	1799	958	2140	1299
0715	Fri 14 Jul	1799	958	2140	1299
0722	Fri 21 Jul	1799	958	2140	1299
0729	Fri 28 Jul	1799	958	2140	1299
0805	Fri 04 Aug	1799	958	2140	1299
0812	Fri 11 Aug	1799	958	2140	1299
0819	Fri 18 Aug	1799	958	2140	1299
0826	Fri 25 Aug	1799	958	2140	1299
0902	Fri 01 Sep	1799	958	2140	1299
0909	Fri 08 Sep	1799	958	2140	1299
0916	Fri 15 Sep	1799	958	2140	1299
0923	Fri 22 Sep	1769	928	2140	1299
0930	Fri 29 Sep	1769	928	2140	1299
1007	Fri 06 Oct	1620	918	—	—
1014	Fri 13 Oct	1620	918	—	—

* For any airfare supplement from your departure city, see list 8 on page 14.

To cover various departure and arrival taxes, $62 per person (subject to change) will be added to your air-inclusive invoice.

Upgrade per person for private facilities in Oberammergau; **(tour 5661):** $30

Single room supplement tour 6060: $300; tour 5660/1*: $250; guaranteed shares: see page 5; no triple room reduction*.
* No singles and triples available in Oberammergau; tour members will be asked to share.

Apollo: LSA/V:COS/
AMADEUS: T - COS/

Sabre: ⊠⊠TOR/COS
Worldspan: @@TS/COS

COSMOS HOTELS

FRANKFURT AREA Astron (ST) at Moerfelden or Maxx (ST) at Langen, **MUNICH** Imperial (T) or Rivoli (T), **SALZBURG** Graml (T) or Turnerwirt (T), **INNSBRUCK** Bonalpina (ST) at Igls or Greif (ST), **ST. MORITZ** Bären (ST), **LUGANO** Beha (T) or Calipso (T) or Carioca (T) or Post Simplon (T), **TÄSCH** Touring (ST) at Visp or Walliserhof (ST), **LAKE LUCERNE** Rössli (T) at Alpnachstad or Seehof (T) at Flüelen.

US 99

Cosmos Tour Brochure *(continued)*

Tour conditions — please read carefully

HOW TO MAKE YOUR RESERVATION

See your travel agent who will handle your reservation and help you make your other travel arrangements.

DEPOSIT AND FINAL PAYMENT

Please make checks or money orders payable to your travel agent. For invoices not exceeding four tour members we accept Visa, Discover/Novus, American Express, and MasterCard. Your payment is not deemed made until it is received by Cosmos.

A non-refundable deposit of $150 per tour and person is required for us to hold seats for you. To secure your space, have your travel agent give your name, credit card number, and address to Cosmos when making your reservation. The deposit forms part of your final payment which is due 45 days prior to departure. For final payment your travel agent will submit a UCC form with your signature, billing address, and home telephone number.

Special deposit conditions apply for groups booking tours including Oberammergau.

Acceptance on the tour is subject to presentation at departure of the Tour Member Certificate evidencing receipt of full payment by Cosmos.

CANCELLATIONS AND CANCELLATION FEES

If cancellation is received by Cosmos more than 45 days prior to departure, the non-refundable deposit will be retained (maximum 20% of total price). For cancellations received within 45 days of departure, the following per person cancellation fees apply:

45-22 days prior to departure: 20% of total price.
21-8 days prior to departure: 30% of total price.
7-1 days prior to departure: 50% of total price.
On departure day and later: 100% of total price.

Cancellation charges also apply to additional accommodations reserved prior to and after the tour.

Special cancellation fees apply for groups booking tours including Oberammergau.

If flight changes are requested after the deposit has been received, or if flights are canceled after tickets are issued, revision fees or airline cancellation charges will be applicable. If an air-inclusive tour is canceled after tickets have been issued, refund will be processed after return of the air tickets.

If Cosmos cancels a tour, we will re-book passengers on the same tour with a different departure date or a similar tour; if Cosmos has confirmed flights on the canceled tour we will confirm flights for the alternate tour. All re-bookings are subject to availability. If the alternate tour is not acceptable, we will refund all monies paid to Cosmos by your travel agent; there is no additional liability. Cosmos cannot assume responsibility for any additional costs or any fees relating to the issuance and/or cancellation of air tickets or other travel arrangements not made through Cosmos.

REVISION FEES

A handling fee of $30 per transaction will be charged for any alteration or revision made to a reservation. A change of tour date or tour itinerary within 45 days of departure will be treated as a cancellation and new booking; regular cancellation fees apply.

MEMBERSHIP

In order to ensure congenial membership, Cosmos reserves the right to accept or reject any person as a tour participant and to expel from the tour any participant whose conduct is deemed incompatible with the interest of the tour group.

TRAVELERS WHO NEED SPECIAL ASSISTANCE

Any disability requiring special attention must be reported to Cosmos at the time the reservation is made. Cosmos will make reasonable attempts to accommodate the special needs of disabled tour members, but is not responsible in the event it is unable to do so, nor is it responsible for any denial of services by carriers, hotels, restaurants, or other independent suppliers. European touring motorcoaches are not equipped with wheelchair ramps. We regret that we cannot provide individual assistance to a tour member for walking, dining, getting on and off motorcoaches, and other transportation vehicles or other personal needs. Travelers who need such assistance, must be accompanied by a qualified companion.

YOUNG TOUR PARTICIPANTS

Tour participants who are less than 18 years old on the tour departure date must be accompanied by an adult; they receive 10% discount on the land tour price. On escorted tours, and cruises starting from Athens we do not accept children under eight years old, because we have found they are too young to enjoy these vacations.

On independent city stays there is no age limit. Land arrangements for infants under two on independent city stays are free of charge, providing parents pay directly to the hotels for food, crib etc. Infants sometimes fly free of charge if they do not occupy a seat, while some airlines charge 10 percent. An airline ticket is always required for the child. Please arrange for this ticket directly with the airline.

SMOKING

Smoking is not allowed on Cosmos motorcoaches or in "guaranteed share" hotel rooms.

TOUR PRICES

Air-inclusive prices are for departures from the USA.

Tour prices are per person, based on two persons sharing a room. Single room supplements and triple room reductions are listed where applicable. All tour prices are based on rates (including foreign exchange rates) known September 1999 and expected to be in effect at the time of departure. They are subject to increase without notice if such rates change prior to departure. For our price guarantee see page 5. Taxes and fees are subject to change without notice.

PASSPORTS

A valid passport is required of all tour participants. A U.S. passport is valid for ten years (children five years).

To apply for passports you can contact either your local passport office, designated federal or state clerk of court, or selected post offices. Of course, your local travel agent will help you to obtain the necessary forms for passport application.

VISAS

At the time of printing, visas for Eastern European countries and Jordan are required of all tour members. U.S. citizens do not require visas for any other country.

For tours requiring visas for U.S. citizens, detailed visa information will be mailed or faxed to your travel agent. Non-U.S. citizens must consult with the appropriate consulates to determine if any visas are needed. Securing any needed visas is the responsibility of the tour participant.

HOTEL ACCOMMODATION

The hotels listed in this brochure will be used on most departures. If a change becomes necessary for any reason, hotels substituted will be equivalent to those shown.

While every effort is made to reserve only twin-bedded rooms, it may occasionally happen that a hotel provides some double-bedded rooms instead. These rooms will be allocated to couples.

Please note that throughout Europe it is standard policy that hotel rooms are not available for check-in before 1 p.m.

PRIVATE BATH AND SINGLE ROOMS

In exceptional cases where private bath or single rooms may not be available as reserved by us, refunds will be made by the tour director. Claims made in this respect cannot be accepted after the tour. "Guaranteed shares" are available; see page 5.

BAGGAGE

Porterage for **one** suitcase on tour is included in the tour price. Due to limited coach capacity, this single bag **should have dimensions not exceeding 30"x18"x10" and weight not exceeding 60 lbs (27kg).**

A charge of US$3 per traveling day will be collected by the tour director if a second piece of baggage is carried, or if the suitcase exceeds the established weight and/or dimensions. International air carriers may also impose fees or require you to remove articles and put them in another bag if weight or size limits on checked or carry-on luggage are exceeded.

Wheeled carry-on cases are not suitable as hand luggage on motorcoaches.

No responsibility is accepted for loss of or damage to baggage or any of the passengers' belongings. Baggage insurance is recommended. See the facing page for an all-inclusive Travel Protection Plan.

TRAVEL DOCUMENTS

Travel documents including any air tickets are sent UPS three to four weeks prior to tour departure, providing full payment has been received; a $7.50 charge per reservation is added for documents requested in advance. To ensure quick and safe receipt of documents, a $7.50 charge per reservation can be added for FedEx delivery in the continental USA. (FedEx is required for reservations made within 45 days of departure.) Please ask your travel agent to tell us at the time of reservation if you prefer UPS or FedEx.

NOT INCLUDED IN THE TOUR PRICE

Federal Inspection Fees for the U.S. Customs and Immigration; International Air Transportation Tax; Agricultural Tax; Security Fee: airport taxes; passports; visas; tips to your tour director, tour driver and local city guides; gratuities on ferries and cruise ships; laundry, beverages and food not on the regular table d'hôte menu (these extra items will be billed to you before leaving the hotel or restaurant); all other items of a personal nature.

OPTIONAL SIGHTSEEING

Excursions, city sightseeing, entrance fees and local guides are not included in the tour price unless specifically noted on each tour page. Apart from sightseeing included in your tour price, there are many opportunities to complete your holiday by signing up for additional sightseeing excursions. These optional excursions may be booked with your tour director on board the motorcoach. Your portfolio of travel documents will specify cost and content of the optional highlights that may be offered during your tour. This enables you to budget accordingly before you leave home.

SERVICE INQUIRIES AFTER THE TOUR

If after returning from the tour you wish to inquire about any tour services provided, please ensure that all correspondence relating to those services is received by Cosmos Quality Control, Group Voyagers Inc. (address below), within 60 days after the tour completion date. This will enable Cosmos to make a timely investigation.

CHANNEL CROSSING

We reserve the right to use "Le Shuttle" services through the Channel Tunnel in either one or both directions.

RESPONSIBILITY

Group Voyagers Inc., d/b/a Cosmos, 5301 S. Federal Circle, Littleton CO80123-2980 (hereinafter referred to as "the Company") is responsible to you in making arrangements for the tour services offered in this brochure, including transportation, sightseeing and hotel accommodations.

The carriers, hotels and other suppliers providing tour services are independent contractors and are not agents, employees or servants of or joint venturers with the Company or its affiliates. All certificates and other travel documents for tour services issued by the Company are subject to the terms and conditions specified by the supplier and to the laws of the countries in which the services are supplied.

If, after tour departure, the services included in the tour cannot be supplied or there are changes in an itinerary for reasons beyond the control of the Company, the Company will arrange for the provision of comparable services. Any resulting additional expense will be payable by tour participants and any resulting saving will be refunded by the Company to tour participants.

The Company reserves the right to accept or reject any person as a tour participant, to expel any tour participant from the tour, to make changes in the itinerary whenever the Company deems it necessary for the comfort, convenience or safety of the tour participants, and to cancel a tour at any time.

The tour participant agrees that neither the Company nor its affiliates shall be liable for any damage, loss (including personal injury, death and property loss) or expense occasioned by any act or omission (including acts or omissions directly or indirectly related to year 2000 computer functioning) of any supplier providing tour services or any insurer or insurance administrator under the Travel Protection Plan, or of any other person.

Legal proceedings against the Company may be instituted only in a state or federal court located within the State of Colorado, and any claim involved in such proceedings shall be decided in accordance with the laws of the State of Colorado. Any legal proceedings against the Company must be commenced within one year following the date of tour completion. Neither the Company nor any affiliate shall in any case be liable for other than compensatory damages, and you hereby waive any right to punitive damages.

No person, other than an authorized representative of the Company, by a document in writing, is authorized to vary, add or waive any term or condition in this brochure, including any term or condition set forth in the preceding provisions.

ROME 2000

The Company reserves the right to cancel in whole or in part Rome sightseeing because of traffic regulations and conditions arising from Holy Year Celebrations. If Rome sightseeing is cancelled in whole or in part, our tour directors will give directions on how to sightsee in Rome independently and will arrange for a refund of the charge for cancelled sightseeing included in the tour price, but we will not accept responsibility for additional costs or claims.

TRADE NAMES

COSMOS is a service mark registered in the U.S. Patent and Trademark Office. CST#2017032-20

138 **US**